CLASSIC MARQUES

David Brown Tractors
1936-1964

ALAN EARNSHAW

NOSTALGIA ROAD

First published by
Transpennine Publishing 1997
Second edition 2000

This edition published by
Crécy Publishing 2013

A CIP record for this book is available from
the British Library

ISBN 9 781908 347084

Printed in Malta by Melita Press

Crécy Publishing Limited
1a Ringway Trading Estate
Shadowmoss Road
Manchester M22 5LH

www.crecy.co.uk

Front Cover: Testing an 850 with an Albion Forage Harvester on bracken in Meltham.

Rear Cover Top: The range of implements soon grew for the Cropmaster range with both the company and other makers jumping on the band-wagon. Here a demonstrator is fitted with a front-mounted splitter.

Rear Cover Bottom: The short wheel-based 2D was widely praised by the various agricultural colleges, and the farming press called it 'the tractor of the future'. A lot were sold in Holland and France as well as around the market gardens near London.

Contents Page: Model 25, 30 and 50 tractors being loaded at Meltham station prior to being exported to Finland.

All photographs David Brown unless otherwise indicated.

ALAN EARNSHAW, author of this book and the founder of Transpennine Publishing (the original publishers of the Nostalgia Road series), died in 2009. This book is reissued now largely as he originally wrote it when first published in 1997 and revised for its second edition in 2000. Apart from editing, no effort has been made to update the book and it stands as a tribute to the enthusiasm of the author for his first employers, a company that engendered a strong loyalty amongst all those involved with it over the years.

Contents

Introduction

The story of the David Brown tractor is one of the most fascinating pieces of British agricultural engineering history, and it began over seven decades ago in the West Riding of Yorkshire. How tractors came to be built in Huddersfield, more famous for worsted cloth, a fine choral society and its football team, is a story that we will recall in due course.

The launch of the first edition of this book at the company's Park Gears Works was just a small part of Brown's continuing support to my research, and it is with grateful thanks that I acknowledge the vital contribution that my former employers have made towards this book. It is also important to acknowledge that this publication is not just down to my solitary endeavour. Indeed, this is the work of many hands and a combination of the personal recollections of many people who were deeply involved with the family firm of David Brown.

I must again acknowledge the assistance rendered by ex-David Brown staff like Herbert E. Ashfield, Albert Berry, Anthony Heath, Leonard Craven, Ron Fisher, John Hudson, Bob Marsh and Derek Marshall and the late Thomas Lazenby. From non-DBT personnel, may I thank Adam Brown (grandson of Sir David), Messrs Gibbs, the late Robin Kedward, Messrs Rickerby & Co, Mike Smart. Bill Smith, Bob Thomas, Alec Winspear and the many other enthusiasts, farmers and sales-people who helped make this book. For my own part, I have had the pleasure of bringing together their recollections, and the pleasant delight of reliving many fond memories.

From infancy David Brown Tractors was a close part of my life; it had to be because we lived right opposite A Block of the Meltham Mills works. When I was old enough to go to school, I walked down Meltham Mills Road past the huge red-brick building known as C Block into the local primary school, which was located directly opposite E Block. Yet, despite the enormous size and complexity of the Meltham Mills works, this was essentially a rural village and the tractor factory fitted snugly into an attractive and deeply wooded valley on the edge of the Pennines. It was an unlikely setting for any large engineering works, but here thousands of tractors were produced between 1939 and 1988.

Meltham Mills and the nearby town of Meltham were dominated by the influences of this engineering giant. Indeed this exacting, but rather benevolent company, touched the lives of thousands of local folk. To work at Brown's was to be part of a large family and, by extension, this family arrangement extended from the works into the surrounding districts. For local lads, the reward for completing our education with good grades meant, or so it seemed, a job for life. I joined the David Brown Corporation as a Commercial Apprentice at the end of the 'swinging 1960s' when the company was at its zenith and when flower power was all the rage.

By this time the firm had grown from very humble beginnings, just over a century earlier, when the first David Brown started a small wooden gear-making shop in Huddersfield. From its inception

The David Brown stand at the 1950 Smithfield Show.

Park Gear Works, Lockwood, around the start of the 20th century, showing the main office block before its extension.

in 1860 the company expanded from employing a handful of people to 16,000 just over a century later. By this time the firm had become an international operation with a turn-over in excess of £55 million and had won the Queen's Award to Industry. For the first four decades David Brown specialised in the production of wooden patterns for firms that were casting gears for local textile machinery manufacturers. However, as technology progressed, these manufacturers began to require more advanced gearing systems for drive delivery; the company saw the opportunity and exploited it. An early innovation was the change from cast-iron to steel, as the demands on gearing systems grew.

By the end of the 19th century, Frank Brown, son of the founder, decided that the firm's Huddersfield premises were much too small for its needs, and a lengthy search was instituted for a new factory. After failing to agree to terms set by the London & North Western Railway for a site at Gledholt, alongside the Huddersfield to Manchester railway, Brown looked around for another site where rail access was available. Thanks to a business acquaintance, William Whiteley, the firm purchased a large country residence, Park House at Lockwood, which was adjacent to the Huddersfield to Sheffield railway. Manufacturing was commenced in the grounds, and the story of the world famous Park Gear Works had begun.

After a period of considerable consolidation, aided by a full order book through World War 1, the firm began to expand on its gear manufacturing activities. In this period Brown's devised and patented the precision worm reduction gear. In the 1920s further developments were made to the precision products range, and the company began to achieve a monopoly in supplying gearboxes to the developing automotive trade — particularly motor lorries and buses. Having successfully survived the Depression, it was able to acquire the properties of other companies that had not been so lucky. It was Frank's son. David, who took the initiative firstly by purchasing the old Cammell Laird Tyre Rolling Mills at Penistone in 1934. Located approximately 12 miles south of the firm's headquarters, the plant was converted into a steel foundry, reducing the need to purchase raw supplies from outside sources.

When an Irish engineer by the name of Harry Ferguson approached the company to help with his ideas for a new farm tractor, David Brown seized the opportunity. Ferguson came from a farming background, but at an early age he left the farm and became an automobile mechanic. He soon became well-known in his locality, due to his exploits with motorcycles and racing cars, but he went on to form his own company repairing tractors, most of which were of American origin. He was a very individual character and quite unlike David Brown, yet the two of them formed a partnership in 1936; between them they produced the first tractor in the world to be equipped with a hydraulic lift and three-point linkage. Sadly the partnership was not harmonious, and it is quite understandable why two extremely capable engineers with completely different (but strong) temperaments should, in the long run, each seek to go their own way. Ferguson's story is another matter, but Brown was adamant that he could and would produce tractors that were both innovative and revolutionary. He saw, all too clearly, the massive changes that were coming in British agriculture.

David and his father argued over the practicality of the plan, to the extent that Frank refused his son the much needed manufacturing space at Lockwood. However, as the Munich crisis developed, David Brown acquired the vacant Meltham Mills. These were located some three miles from Lockwood but benefited from being connected by a branch railway. Throughout the war this factory played a vital role in war production, with tank gearboxes, aero-gears and military tractors being produced alongside the agricultural tractor the VAK1. As peace returned the flood gates opened and by 1948 the firm was making and selling 100 tractors a week. As the years progressed, the company grew into a corporation, and new gear plants were acquired or opened at Sunderland, Salford, Solihull and north London.

By the time I joined the company, the use of the gearing division's products was found in the aircraft, automotive and railway industries, steel mills, pulp mills, paper mills, sugar mills, armoured fighting vehicles and ship building to name but a few. It also owned the famous luxury and sporting car manufacturers Aston-Martin Lagonda and the shipbuilding firms of John L. Thornycroft Ltd and Vospers Ltd. Other divisions of the company produced pumps, industrial heating equipment, honing equipment, microwave ovens, interior design and furnishing contracts and industrial oil burning equipment. It was an empire presided over by David (now a knight of the realm), and an army of able assistants that included his son, also called David (and often referred to as David Brown junior).

The tractor group was a major operation in its own right and it had 10 subsidiary companies. The main one was Harrison, McGregor & Guest Ltd at the Albion Works, Leigh, Lancashire. Overseas companies were found in Australia, Ireland, South Africa, Eire, the USA, West Germany and Denmark. It was also the largest British-owned producer of agricultural tractors, with 80% of the output going for export. The dealer network numbered some 2,508 agents in 100 lands. It was an organisation that one could be proud to be a part of and yet it was still run as a small family firm.

The late Alan Earnshaw

In at the Start: 1936-1939

LEONARD CRAVEN

I FIND it hard to believe that it is now more than 60 years since I was given the unique opportunity to take an active part in constructing the first small batch of what was then, the revolutionary farm tractor invented by Harry Ferguson, and built and marketed in conjunction with the David Brown organisation. It subsequently proved to be a revolution in the world of agriculture as the demand for farm mechanisation developed. It was in spring 1936 that I made my way into one of the massive machine shops of the Park Works factory. David Browns were acknowledged to be 'the World's Finest Gear Makers', and there were literally hundreds of metalworking machines operating in this immense one-storey building.

One corner had been cleared however and an area of about 20sq yd was now occupied by half a dozen fitters' benches and an untidy stack of material. From this pile of parts a small band of four or five fitters were endeavouring to put together the very first batch of tractors to come off the line. There were also five Coventry Climax 'E' type engines (which were fitted as standard to the first 350 tractors). Three of these had been fitted with a bell-housing and clutch mechanism and were in the process of being mated up with transmission and rear axle units that had been constructed on adjacent benches. The foreman, Harry Pilkington, and his fitters were experiencing some difficulty in finding the necessary parts.

The problem was that all the parts had been dumped in an untidy heap of material on the shop floor. It was my duty to identify the components, match them up to the delivery notes and place them in the metal bins that had been temporarily erected on the site. The first building sanction was for 100 tractors, and material ordered from outside suppliers was already arriving in an ever-increasing stream. By the time that the first five tractors were ready, it was evident that more space was needed.

Therefore, the operation was transferred to the upper three floors of what had been the Automobile Gearbox plant. The first floor became the tractor assembly area, the second eventually housed the engine assembly, implements were built on the third and the fourth was given over to painting and 'finishing'. Additional labour was recruited, mostly from the ranks of the workforce of the Karrier Motors, who had recently been made redundant.

The manager was Harold Thompson, who had been recruited from the Midlands. However, the man with the most difficult job was Mr Cosgrave, who was responsible for organising a steady flow of the right material (at the right time) to the tractor assembly line. The completed tractors were transferred to Harry Ferguson's marketing and distribution premises, which were located in the former Karrier Works in nearby Cable Street.

Quite frequently, Ferguson and John Chambers, together with their henchmen Greer and Sands, visited the assembly line, where they became known as 'the Cable Street Gang'. Although their visits were usually in connection with some technical problem, they did tend to interfere somewhat with the normal operations. Consequently, over the months, their welcome became less cordial. Harry Ferguson was undoubtedly a genius, but he had his eccentricities which were difficult to understand, and quite often absolutely unacceptable

Ferguson-Brown tractor No 1, seen here, is preserved at the Massey-Ferguson Heritage Centre, Banner Lane, Coventry. Our thanks to Massey Fergsuon for the kind use of this picture.

The first Ferguson-Brown tractors were fitted with the Coventry Climax engine, but David Brown wanted to produce his own engine, the prototype of which is seen here under test. The new-power unit was suitable for petrol/TVO fuel and had a cylinder bore of $3^{1}/_{8}$in as opposed to $3^{1}/_{4}$in on the Climax; the oil sump was larger and an oil-bath air filter fitted to combat dusty working conditions.

This picture of No 1 is taken up near Castle Hill above Huddersfield, with some of the team who put together the first Ferguson-Brown tractor. Those involved with the first tractors were Fred Armitage, Harry Brown, John Cook, Harold Idle, Bill Wallace, Bernard North, Harry Dobson, Jeff Lee, Ernest Kenyan, Jimmy Milnes, Jim Kenny, Godwin Atkinson and Bill Dearnley in the assembly team. Sam Crosland and Harry Hall were general labourers, and the apprentices were Norman Calvert, Leslie Nunns, Norman Whitley and Trevor Noble. Harold Hawkes and Harry Lockley were the painters and the quality control inspector was Emil Moes, an expatriate Belgian

Left: Harry Ferguson wanted the tractor to he simply called the 'Ferguson', hut when it was launched to the press by the DB Publicity Department its name had been changed to the 'Ferguson-Brown' and this led to the first of many disagreements. Brown, therefore, decided to build his own tractor, and a stylish wooden mock-up was made in great secrecy.

Right: As time went by, the first David Brown tractor was built and painted in a grey scheme to confuse any onlookers. It was then tested in great secrecy around the moors of Meltham in early 1939 and later sent to work on a farm in North Yorkshire. It is seen here with the registration plate BVH 10.

to more ordinary people. One can give some credence to his fetish 'that under no consideration must the weight of his tractor exceed that of a plough horse' — after all, there was the problem of soil compression! The majority of the nuts and bolts on the Ferguson-Brown products had either $7/16$in or $5/8$in BSF thread, but the maestro was not satisfied with the reliability of ordinary standard steel bolts. He insisted on using only special 'Hitensile' bolts, and all the nuts had to be casehardened in the Heat Treatment Department.

Such was his obsession with ensuring the reliability of bolted components, that he could frequently be seen, particularly in the implement assembly shop, literally hanging (with his feet off the ground) onto a specially made five-foot extension welded on to an engineer's spanner — making sure that the nut was securely tightened! Many of the highly experienced fitters on the workforce protested that this was contrary to the ethics of good engineering. Some even refused point blank to use anything but the standard spanner, creating quite a tricky situation for the personnel department. One is tempted to wonder if there could be some link with the fact that the Ferguson operation over the years moved from David Browns to Ford, then to Standard and finally from Standard to Massey Harris?

By the end of the year the first 100 tractors had been built and the Ferguson team had succeeded in creating a growing demand for the product in a market that had a traditional reputation of resistance to innovation. A further build order for 250 tractors and sets of implements ensured continuity of the operation. The new engine assembly department was installed on the second floor, and by the time the 350th tractor rolled off the line, the David Brown engine was available to be fitted as standard to the next sanction for 500 tractors.

The marketing team were really getting its message across, and the demand for this innovative tractor continued to increase by leaps and bounds. Local authorities discovered that this lively and highly manoeuvrable machine was eminently suitable for a variety of urban applications in parks, gardens and cemeteries. When fitted with a rotary brush it was also ideal for street cleansing operations. There was even an order for four tractors to be delivered to a customer in South Africa to operate underground in diamond mines.

A number of tractors had been exported to Scandinavia to be used in forestry work, but the strain imposed on the aluminium gearbox casing resulted in a large proportion of the vehicles literally 'breaking their backs'. The David Brown engineers prescribed the use of a steel or cast-iron gearbox casing, but the Ferguson lobby was adamant in its rejection of this, as this would increase the weight of the machine beyond the limits specified by its inventor

Eventually a compromise was agreed; the material specification for the gearbox was changed to RR50 — a very expensive light alloy! Purely out of interest, the part number of the modified component was G110. Many of the customers for the tractor were 'first time' buyers, and they were taking the first step to mechanisation by acquiring a tractor to take over some of the work formerly done by horses. There were some funny anecdotes brought back to the factory by the field service operators: like the farmer who always shouted 'Gee up!' when starting to move, and 'Whoa!' when stopping or applying the brakes; and one who, when reporting a radiator leak, said 'She be awful thirsty of late'.

The name was by now firmly established in the UK, and an ever-increasing flow of orders resulted in a further extension of the building sanction for another 500 units. In the early part of 1938 the production target of 10 tractors per week was finally achieved. Significantly, although no further building sanction for the Ferguson-Brown tractor was issued, the David Brown organisation purchased the extensive Meltham Mills factory site with the declared intention of using it as a tractor manufacturing plant.

There had been a small but persistent demand for a stronger and more durable gearbox housing in spite of the concessionary RR50 component approved by the Ferguson team. In response to external pressures our engineers in conjunction with Brown's foundry at Penistone produced about a dozen 'meehanite' cast-iron gearbox cases to be supplied to selected customers. However, when Brown pressed Ferguson to make these improvements in the Ferguson-Brown, his partner would not alter his design one little bit. Thereafter the rift turned into an unbridgeable chasm, and David Brown decided to break the partnership and produce his own tractor. Yet, until such time as that could be produced, the Ferguson-Brown continued in production.

A total of 350 of the model were produced over a period of three years. The last 14 being completed at Meltham Mills some months after the new David Brown VAK1 tractor had made its triumphal debut at the 1939 Royal Agricultural Society's show at Windsor. Ferguson was busying himself in America, meanwhile, having 'meaningful discussions' with Henry Ford. It can be rightly said that the Ferguson-Brown tractor revolutionised the British agricultural equipment manufacturing industry, and it was the first stage in two great marques. As time progressed the differences grew and, as Herbert Ashfield recalls, 'when the Ferguson-Brown tractors were not selling particularly well. David Brown began to enquire why!' It was therefore shown to him that the model needed a number of modifications to make it acceptable to the majority of British farmers.

Whereas the official records account for 1,350 Ferguson-Browns being produced we can now reveal that, in actual fact, 1,351 of these pioneering tractors were made and sold! On this point Leonard Craven concludes: 'In the early part of 1940, a very special friend of "the Boss" expressed a desire for one of these now "out of production" machines, and as a very special favour it was decided to make one from the Replacement Parts Department stock. I know that this happened because I was the storekeeper who issued the parts to the Service workshop for assembly.'

Model Types

VAK 1: 1939-1945

AS THE problems with Ferguson became insoluble, David Brown's design team began the first tentative steps toward the production of its own, independent tractor. However, as work on the Ferguson-Brown was still continuing at Park Works, the project had to be carried out without any publicity. Before commencing this project, David Brown had met Alex Taub of General Motors who provided invaluable advice and encouragement. This had finally convinced Brown that his new engine should be made to a completely new design, using overhead valves and wet sleeves. Accordingly, David Brown engaged a designer called Albert Kersey, who he secreted away in an isolated drawing office at Park Works.

To maintain the secrecy, the design team referred to their new project by a clandestine code name, VAK1 (Vehicle Agricultural Kerosene One). Leonard Craven remembers the time well, writing: 'During 1938 it became evident that all was not well at the top. Visits by Ferguson and "the Cable Street gang" became more sporadic, and the former spirit of camaraderie and comradeship was noticeably at a premium. What was more significant however was the "cloak and dagger" activity on the top floor, which was virtually designated a "No Go" area to all but the team of David Brown engineers who were examining in great detail tractors made by other manufacturers. I remember seeing Ford, John Deere, Allis Chalmers and Massey Harris machines on various occasions!'

This culminated in the erection of a full sized 'dummy' model of a machine, which eventually emerged as the new David Brown tractor. The new David Brown engine was completed on 13 December 1938 and it ran on its test-bed with considerable ease — which was obviously a great relief to all concerned! The next stage was the completion of the prototype tractor, so the small 'research and development' team worked on in secret — often working long into the dark winter evenings. As the work on the machine neared completion one evening in January, David Brown told his men to knock off at midnight and finish it off the next day. However, after he had gone, they all decided to carry on until the tractor was done.

They worked until the small hours to complete the final adjustments and then, on finishing the tractor, Ernest Kenyon got the bright idea to drive it up to David Brown's house, Durker Roods at Meltham, so that the 'boss' could see it running. It is reputed that the great man was awakened around 3am by the revving engine and a group of grinning, cheering men. Brown then came down in dressing gown, pyjamas and slippers to see his first machine and then they all toasted the success of the tractor with his best malt whisky.

More work was to be done on the tractor, and several modifications were indicated after its initial field tests. These tests were quite extreme and, as Leonard Craven recalls: 'It was decided to test the tractor to destruction, to see which components gave up first. In its grey paint it was taken out on a circuit around Meltham which took it up Wessendenhead Road to the Isle of Skye Hotel; from there it followed the Saddleworth to Holmfirth road back to

The first VAK1 that was produced for display set a trend for all models that were to be later put on show! These show tractors all had extra detail, and all the external bolt heads that were visible had bright chromium-plated bolts fitted. The same bright finish was applied to the headlamps and to other small parts, though these would have normally been painted red or black. Bright, stylish and attractive they may have been, but to the down-to-earth Yorkshiremen who built them, they were known inside the works as the 'pansy tractors'.

With a lease for the mills secured on favourable terms, orders at hand for the VAK1, and a good design and engineering team established, the tractor operation moved to the 400,000sq ft of the Meltham Mills factory. It is believed that Frank Brown told his son that he would offer a limited amount of support. The first production line, pictured here in 1942, was soon underway.

Left: With its 3.5in bore petrol or TVO engine and four-speed gearbox, some 5,350 VAK1s were to be produced between 1939 and 1945, including some Utility versions. The VAK demonstrator is seen at work on threshing duties during 1943 in a picture that is thought to have been taken in Buckinghamshire.

Above: The rear end of the prototype VAK1; it was never produced in this form.

Left: A Utility version of the VAK1 with the bullet-hole grille in 1943, although Utility models rarely featured rubber tyres.

Below: A VAK1 in use for ARP/NFS duties in May 1940.

the Ford Inn from where it returned to Meltham.' It was a demanding route that reached an altitude of 1,506ft (460m) above sea level, and on one or two occasions it was actually buried deep into snow-drifts and had to be recovered. In view of the secrecy it was run on this route at night, an unenviable task shared by Bill Harrison and a small team of drivers who braved the winter weather on the Pennine moors.

The tractor was, however, to be kept running for 24 hours a day and some of the testing was carried out on David Brown's own land or in the quarries at Royd Edge. Then, with even more secrecy, the tractor was taken to a farm at Middleton Tyas in the North Riding where it was put under further stress and strain. Fortunately, these tests and the subsequent improvements were concluded just in time for a restyled VAK1 to be prepared for the 1939 Royal Agricultural Show, which was held at Windsor Great Park that July. The biggest difficulty to be faced by the team was actually what colour to paint its new tractor, and the obvious choice of brown was widely discussed and almost equally rejected. When the decision over the colour scheme became heated, it is said that Brown sent for his red hunting jacket, and then threw this on to the tractor and said 'paint it that colour'. This task was duly completed by Harold Hawkes and Harry Lockley, the company's two tractor painters. Thus was born the unusual and distinctive livery that, quite appropriately, was known to all and sundry as 'hunting pink'.

As Herbert Ashfield recalls: 'When we were making the Ferguson-Brown we had the advantage of Ferguson patents but after the split we had to get round these; they were mainly concerned with getting weight transfer from the plough to the tractor's rear wheels, and also with getting the plough to follow. We got over the depth control problem by putting an adjustable land wheel on the implement that completely overcame that part of the patent. The convergent linkage problem was solved by someone coming up with the brilliant idea of parallel linkage and a z-cross shaft. This meant that instead of the inclination being on the links, it was put on the cross shaft, so when the plough moved off centre the z-shaft fetched it back. That was our way of getting around the Ferguson patents, but virtually every other tractor manufacturer, including Ford (after a spectacular law suit), paid him a royalty on his convergent linkage patents.

'Another matter was the original bolt-on power lift that used the Ferguson pump and a number of Ferguson parts. We decided to put our own control valve on the VAK1 to get round the patent, but this wasn't really satisfactory. We eventually got the power lift right on the VAK1, but this wasn't until about the time when we went on to the Cropmaster. So, although we had our trials with the power lift, we did avoid the Ferguson patents; for example, one of these showed that their control valve was on the suction side, so we put our control valve on the delivery side and got over that.'

The VAK1 made its way to its first public appearance by rail, being sent by the LMS from Meltham station. The tractors that were sent were all sheeted over, as great efforts were made to conceal their actual appearance until their arrival at the show ground. However, after the wagons arrived at the GWR station yard in Windsor, it was found that the paintwork on the bonnets had been badly rubbed by the heavy tarpaulin sheets that were used on the railways. Very hasty arrangements had to be made for coach painters to be hired locally so that the problem could be resolved in time for pristine tractors to be shown on the stand. The stand of David Brown Tractors Ltd, Huddersfield, carried both Ferguson advertising banners and Ferguson-Brown tractors, but the main focus for attention was undoubtedly the VAK1. In its hunting pink livery and with a cockpit arrangement for the driver, it was a truly resplendent and stylish tractor. It was also in stark contrast to most of the other tractors then being displayed, and as a consequence it was an immediate success with both the farming press and those who would actually use it.

It is known that orders for 3,000+ tractors were taken, though Ferguson's reaction on seeing the VAK1 is said to be entirely unprintable. The outbreak of war in September 1939 coincided with the formal break up of the Brown/Ferguson partnership. Ferguson would have nothing to do with David Brown's new model, so Brown bought out Ferguson's shares (and those of his friends), paying them pound for pound on their investment. The threat of war considerably strengthened Brown's position, as he believed that hostilities would create a massive demand for all types of tractor.

Nor was Brown idle in this period and he succeeded in getting a great deal of 'war work' but this work nearly made his dream of tractors stillborn. At the time the war began, tractor production was still being carried out at Park Works, for the Meltham Mills factory did not exist as such, save as a collection of large abandoned buildings full of redundant textile machinery. After a massive clearing up operation, work began in fitting out the factory for engineering purposes, but the Ministry of Supply was already becoming increasingly reluctant to allow supplies of steel for the manufacture of tractors. In one conversation, a supply officer told David Brown 'why do farmers need tractors, they've used horses for centuries'.

VTK1 AND VIG1: 1941-1949

A factor in the official attitude against tractor manufacture in this country was due to the fact that American tractors were available to Britain via the Lease-Lend scheme, whereas military equipment was not. Herbert Ashfield confirms this: 'When I started, the VAK1 was on ration as they were only allowed to make so many agricultural tractors a week. They had contracts for Air Ministry tractors, the VIG1, for which there was an insatiable demand. It didn't matter how many they made, because more were always needed. However, on the back of this production they allowed us to make a set number of agricultural tractors. This was primarily because we used mounted implements behind the VAK1 and these only used about a third of the steel that a conventional implement needed. There was a big demand for ploughs because, due to the massive increase in food production, a lot of pre-war ploughs were rapidly wearing out. As the Government was having to allocate materials to replace them, it decided to send the steel to us as we could produce a plough for the VAK1 for about a third of the cost of a conventional trailed implement.

'The VAK1 prospered because of this and we made a total of 5,000 in the period of 1940-44. That's around 1,000 a year — not bad going for the war years.' Indeed it was not bad going at all but already a successor for the VAK1 was becoming essential if the company was to build on this success and the last build order for this model was sanctioned in October 1944.

With the work that David Brown Gears was doing on tank transmissions in the 1930s and the firm's development into agricultural products, it is not surprising that the company would apply this technology to military use in the form of a tracked tractor.

Actually, David Brown had wanted to start producing a tracked tractor shortly after his split with Harry Ferguson, but he was initially prevented from doing so because of the difficulties with his father over space at Lockwood, the subsequent move to Meltham Mills and the outbreak of war. Yet he held this goal constantly in mind in the late 1930s because he had a strong idea that the country would soon be crying out for tracked vehicles as well as agricultural tractors.

When the Ministry of Supply assessed the output potential of Meltham Mills, it was patently obvious that the two areas of war production where David Brown could provide both experience and capacity would be the manufacture of tank gearboxes and aero gears/components. Indeed from 1940 to 1945, Meltham Mills turned out 10,000 tank transmissions, 125,000 aero gears, and 6,000 hydraulic pumps for aircraft.

However, the Minister for Aircraft Production (Lord Beaverbrook) argued with Winston Churchill that the tractors he needed for towing medium to heavy bombers could not be acquired by Lease-Lend under the terms of the Stockholm Convention, which outlined the issues of neutrality. As the aerodrome construction programme was then considered to be of the utmost national importance, a decision was taken to order a tracked vehicle that could then be later used for towing duties. As Herbert Ashfield remembers: 'The original aircraft tracklayer, the VTK1, may have been a good idea on

The story of the RAF tracklayer seen here near Meltham Mills Bar is quite fascinating, as it was designed to fulfil the Ministry's concept of a dual-purpose tractor with a powerful winch, which could he used either in aerodrome construction or in aircraft towing. Yet both of these roles were, in many ways, completely incompatible with one another. As J. C. R. Birney, then Sales Manager of David Brown, wrote in *Tractor News* at the end of the war: 'The machine was a bastard — in more ways than one.' The design had been rapidly evolved in conjunction with experts from the RAF and it resulted in what was little more than a tracked version of the VAK1. Whilst the tractor performed its tests reasonably well, in service the machine was far from ideal.

A wheeled aircraft towing tractor or, in official parlance, the Vehicle Industrial Government (VIG). It was originally thought to be a conversion of a VTK1 but it has been discovered that this was built as a special for evaluation by the RAF. A Hesford winch and large sprag were fitted at the rear.

The front-mounted Hesford winch on an Air Ministry tracklayer. According to RAF records some tracklayers had rear-mounted winches and a few had both front and rear.

paper, but unfortunately it was so slow that it wasn't really a practical proposition on a busy aerodrome. It had been conceived by people whose idea of an airfield was literally a field, and a tracklayer was not really what was needed at all. Our model had a top speed of five miles an hour, but at anything over this it would shake itself to bits. Sometimes it had to tow an aircraft over a mile, and it took too much time to do this.'

Indeed, in many other ways it was proving itself to be quite unsuitable for its intended purpose, because when they began using crawlers for aircraft towing or bombing up procedures, they found that the metal crawler tracks were not doing a lot of good to the runways and aprons. The Ministry soon decided that it wasn't a crawler that was wanted after all but a wheeled tractor!

All the tracked machines were recalled to Meltham and plans were rapidly drawn up to convert them to wheeled tractors. As these were returned to the works, large numbers of them began building up in the goods yard at Meltham station and they were soon found to be clogging up the space needed for the tank transmissions that were being brought in for gearbox work, not to mention the tractors. They then began to build up at Lockwood station, then Honley, and finally at the Penistone works until the time could be found to convert them.

Herbert Ashfield recalls the decision to convert the tractors for both industrial and agricultural use, stating: 'Nearly all the VTK1s were sent back and converted to wheeled tractors, so that alongside the VAK1 and VAK1A we were offering an industrial tractor, which we were able to achieve by modifying Air Ministry tracklayers and tractors for civilian use. After the war was over, we got a lot back and converted them for peaceful use, turning them into threshing tractors.' Some of the salesmen were often known to quote a little bit of the Bible when selling them for threshing tractors as they said they were figuratively fulfilling the scripture in Isaiah 2 verse 4 which says 'they shall pound their swords into hoes and their spears into pruning hooks'.

A works photograph, dated 1946, of the 'Thresherman' model.

The next stage in development and the official photo album describes it as a 'prototype' heavy industrial model for sale in factory and municipal applications.

In all some 185 VTK1s were poduced, and a large number of these were reworked into conventional wheeled tractors. When the combined production of the Air Ministry and VIG1/100 tractors are taken into consideration, the total production run was 2,400, which was almost half the production figure on the VAK1 and two-thirds the total production of the VAK1A, yet these sturdy, handsome looking tractors are often largely ignored in accounts of the company's early days. Based on VAK1 and 1A tractors, these heavy industrial models had the same 37bhp petrol engine but were fitted with a low-speed final drive for towing. Some were fitted with conventional clutches, but others were provided with fluid drive torque converters. At least four of these tractors were developed as shunting tractors and one, known colloquially as 'Muffin The Mule', spent years shunting the internal railway system at the company's Penistone Works.

VAK1A: 1945-1947

In 1943 G. S. Reekie set out David Brown's development position saying: 'Our agricultural and industrial machines will be just as vital after the War as in the present circumstances and the plant and equipment is therefore poised for quick expansion, as soon as more stable conditions permit the divergence of materials to the constructive purposes of peace. Given the freedom of action we should be in a position to make a very large contribution towards the large number of tractors that the Ministry of Agriculture estimate to be the annual post-war requirements for the British Isles.'

While the main efforts of the company were concentrated on the VAK1 and military requirements throughout the war, design work went on and an improved agricultural tractor, the VAK2, was conceived for peacetime conditions. The four main improvements envisaged for this model were: a combined inlet and exhaust manifold to give better idling on kerosene; a gearbox with six forward and two reverse speeds; a hydraulic system that was inbuilt instead of optional: and, more robust final drives.

Yet this model never came to fruition, as sales in post-war Britain were very buoyant and all the production capacity was needed to fulfil orders for VAK1s. Indeed, a continuing restriction in the supplies of various raw materials coupled with the national austerity period necessitated the continuing production of this model. Therefore, the company found it very hard to institute the much needed changes that it both wanted and had to make. However, with the decision taken not to produce the VAK2, the company opted to introduce progressively the improvements it had decided to embody in this tractor into a modified version of the VAK1.

Thus was born the VAK1A, which appeared in early spring 1945. In this model the improved inlet and manifold were incorporated, although the other three features were not to appear for a further three years when the VAK1C was introduced. This was the first tractor that had got all the bugs out of it, although in fairness the teething problems in the VAK1 had been perpetuated by the war that gave no opportunity for modification.

After the war the demand was for more tractors at a time when farmers were wanting increased horse power and diesel engines. The war had really changed things: farming, manufacturing, popular perceptions and, above all, ideas at David Brown. Tom Lazenby commented: 'Most times we were overcoming problems that had arisen between 1939 and 1945; sometimes these were production problems, or service problems and sometimes even sales problems, all of which were holding back the

A David Brown VAK1 tractor – the first type to be completely designed and built by the company.

tractors at various times. Now around this time we had a market research programme undertaken, which had told us that the market for tractors was at least a 100,000 a year in Great Britain. Nobody in Britain had the capacity for that production, so a great deal of the tractors would have to be imported, though David Brown reckoned we could easily make and sell one hundred tractors a week. I would have thought that we were the only people in the tractor business that knew what the demand was likely to be, and we set our stall out to capture the potential business that we had calculated from the rate at which it was judged that farmers would change from horses to tractors.'

It was abundantly clear that, in this time of change, the VAK, hastily introduced and still suffering from basic shortcomings in the original design, would have to be modified if the company was going to break into the tractor market in a big way. Herbert Ashfield recalls how it came about: 'By the end of the war, the days of the VAK1 were coming to an end as it was only natural they should, because it had been made in a fair hurry in 1939 and its short-comings were well known by 1944. After the VAK2 tractor was dropped, we decided to modify the VAK1 and the idea was to produce further models known as the 1A, 1B, 1C and 1D.

An early model VAK1A seen at the junction of Mill Bank and Meltham Mills roads in November 1945. Altogether 5,350 VAK1As were produced at Meltham Mills, with a final batch of 352 being sanctioned at the end of January 1947. The last VAK1A (No 9852) rolled down the assembly line in June 1947 in the midst of a string of VAK1Cs, which had come into production two months earlier. The VAK1A had been an admirable stopgap, but it was the advent of its successor that would really put David Brown's name into the list of all-time great tractor manufacturers.

In grey primer, this unique VAK1A has been identified as having been fitted with engine modifications planned for the VAK1C, and code-named the VAK1A/B.

'The main problems with the VAK1 were associated with the manifold and the fact that you had to run it quite a while on petrol, before switching over to paraffin; even then, when it idled, it used to pop and back-fire. It was quite a problem so one of the first things we did was to put in a new manifold and divert the exhaust round the intake, so that the exhaust warmed the intake air. With this, once it had warmed up, it would idle without any trouble. At the same time Ford tractors were having a great deal of trouble with paraffin running down the cylinder walls causing a lot of wear, but with the new manifold we didn't get any of these problems. We also redesigned the transmission, and the power lift and we were well satisfied that the VAK1A would carry us through the next couple of years until things became a bit more settled. Unfortunately, the 1B, which was the tractor with a new gearbox, didn't go ahead as sales of the 1A did very well indeed and production of this model ran a lot longer than we ever thought it would.'

As with the VAK1, the 3.5in bore engine was petrol or TVO, and it had a four-speed gearbox and all-speed governors, though an optional six-speed gearbox was introduced in 1948. In 1949 Sales Manager J. C. R. Birney wrote: 'In view of the large numbers of the earlier David Brown models that were still in service, the firm offered a conversion kit for all its TVO engines. This was available at about one-third of the price of a new engine, it prolonged the life of many of those tractors and it bred a new era of brand loyalty to the David Brown Marque.'

VAK1C Cropmaster: 1947-1964

One of the most famous models in the David Brown stable was the VAK1C or the Cropmaster as it was better known. In total some 59,800 were manufactured, making this series of tractor numerically second only to the 990 models. The VAK1C was introduced in April 1947 in time for the round of summer agricultural shows, but David Brown said that he wanted his new tractor to be the star at its first show. Accordingly, the Sales Department came up with a bright idea for its launch, and it decided to have its own show exclusively featuring the equipment made by David Brown and those companies with whom it were associated. This was held on land just off the Harrogate to Pateley Bridge road, and it became known as the Harrogate Convention. When the Cropmaster was presented to the farming public at this event that April, it was billed as the tractor that embodied all the four major improvements that the company had intended to put into the VAK2. It had intended that a VAK1B would be built to incorporate a six-speed gearbox, but it was never introduced and this facility only became available as an optional extra on the VAK1A. Yet the success of these six-speed VAK1As encouraged the Sales Department, and in turn this prompted the firm to move on to the VAK1C.

This development firmly pushed the proposed VAK2 into the realms of a 'might have been', and the decision to carry on the VAK1 designation was taken because the 1C embodied so many features of its two predecessors. It is also worth mentioning the decision to introduce the name Cropmaster rather than the simple alpha-numerical designation that had been hitherto employed. This came about as a consequence of the development of the Marketing Department, which brought its influence to bear on how the company's models were presented. At this time it hit on the 'master' concept, and designations such as 'Cropmaster', 'Taskmaster' and 'Trackmaster' were born. Around the same time, David Brown decided that his name should also appear in large letters on the tractor, as he felt that the world should know that he was the originator of the red tractors. Some may consider this conceited, but he was only exploiting his name and reputation in the same way the Ferguson and Ford were exploiting their names.

The range of implements available with the Cropmaster also grew, and in this the VAK1C became a popular British farm tractor and it greatly speeded up post-war farming mechanisation. Herbert Ashfield writes: 'The 3.5in bore 35.0bhp VAK1C included our own power lift, which we made inbuilt. This was done because one of the problems with selling the original Ferguson was that a farmer had to buy a tractor plus a set of implements. They didn't like it because they wanted to use their own ploughs and trailed implements, but Ferguson wouldn't make any provision for using their old equipment. So if a farmer didn't buy a set of implements the tractor was virtually useless! It was one of the points that David Brown fell out with him on and he said to his design team "Well, why can't we have a draw-bar and then the farmers could hitch up their old trailed ploughs." So on the VAK1 they made provision for the trailed implements, but you've got to remember that there were no mounted implements in those days. So, if you sold a tractor suited for mounted

The prototype Cropmaster seen on the Meltham Mills football ground. The picture was taken before the large 'David Brown' lettering was applied to the bonnet tinwork.

implements, you had to sell mounted implements. Well, we couldn't make enough mounted implements to meet the demand, so our tractor was made with a button-on power lift. Because of this we could sell the tractor with or without a power lift on it, as it still had a drawbar suitable for trailed implements. When we got the 1C we made the inbuilt power lift so it was suitable for trailed implements or mounted implements. In a way the 1C was the big brother to the 1A and, because it was so versatile, we sold so many. But it was the chance to change from a petrol/TVO engine which made such a big difference.'

The VAK1C became available as a 31.5bhp diesel-engined variety in 1949, with the first units being tested in the spring prior to an autumn launch just ahead of the Smithfield Show. Tom Lazenby noted the introduction of the Cropmaster Diesel with some pride: 'The Cropmaster was a grand little tractor, but the Cropmaster Diesel (when it came in) was magnificent and we could sell that like hot cakes.

'I remember when we launched the diesel at the Smithfield Show. Ford's Sales Manager at the time, Frankie Daniels, came up to me and said "I wish we had that." So I took him to have a closer look at it and when we turned the engine over he said "it's marvellous, it runs just like a sewing machine — that's what we want, not an old slab-sided design like ours. Imagine, if you took a good engine like that and put it in the Fordson Major." So we went over and looked at his tractor, and with barely concealed envy he said "It's 25 years out of date this and it needs a thumping bag of tricks in here to improve it. I've seen your engine before of course, and I told the boss [at Ford] if you want to see what's wrong with our engines, go up to Yorkshire and have a look at a real tractor, the Cropmaster diesel." I don't think we could have got any higher praise than that!'

The Cropmaster sold very well, and between 1947 and 1953 the firm made a number of variants. One of the first was the Cropmaster M, a model without hydraulic lift, which was available from April 1947 with the standard engine and as a diesel variant from June 1950.

In all, approaching 5,000 Super Cropmasters were built before the model was discontinued at the end of 1952. As there was a demand for low-clearance and narrow tractors, there was also an emerging demand for tractors with a high clearance, and as a consequence the Prairie version of the Cropmaster emerged in October 1951. Tom Lazenby noted the introduction of this variant: 'When we brought in the Prairie tractor it was aimed at the Canadian and United States market, and we had to make it look a bit different. So we got round a few ideas and tarted up the tractor; you know, different wings, wide mudguards and single seats, which we hoped would kid the Americans that we'd got something really special for them.' The Prairie model did have a very striking appearance, a fact that was much remarked on when it appeared (once again) in time for the Smithfield Show in the December.

A 34.5bhp diesel version was brought out the following autumn and, unlike the Vineyard diesel, sold reasonably well. In fact the Cropmaster Prairie Diesel actually accounted for about a third of the total production figures of this dependable variant. Other versions of the Cropmaster appeared in industrial form (Taskmaster) and as a tracked version (Trackmaster). In all 59,800 Cropmasters were produced before it was superseded by stripped down versions which appeared in 1953 in response to competition brought about by the mass production of Ford and Ferguson tractors.

The Cropmaster diesel was a unique first for the company as it became the first major tractor manufacturer in Britain to launch its own make diesel engine. Yet, this had long been a goal of the company and, when designing the VAK1 engine, David Brown and Albert Kersey had shown the engine plans to Harry Ricardo, who was one of the leading consultants on diesel engines in the 1930s. Brown asked Ricardo what modifications would be required to the design if the engine were ever dieselised, and he was advised to strengthen the camshafts and connecting rods. The tooling for the VAK1 engine included these modifications, and this saved much time and money when the market for introducing a diesel engine finally developed.

Hardly the most popular variant of the Cropmaster, this tricycle model was developed mainly with a view for sales in the North American market.

The range of implements soon grew for the Cropmaster range with both the company and other makers jumping on the band-wagon. Here a demonstrator is fitted with a front-mounted splitter.

TRACKLAYERS: 1942-1963

As we have seen earlier, the first attempt of David Brown into the crawler market was hardly a roaring success, as the VTK1 was really an abysmal failure. But the company had invested a substantial amount of time and money into the crawler production. Fortunately, one of the RAF tracklayers had been loaned some months earlier to the Royal Engineers for work on sea defences in East Anglia.

They were delighted with what they had seen, as it showed that at least one British manufacturer had the potential to make a crawler tractor and this would help them get round the strict embargo on buying equipment for military purposes from countries that were still neutral at the time. True, American-made crawlers were being purchased, but technically it was illegal to use these for any sort of military work. Thus, in 1942, was born the DB4 a 38.5hp crawler that was fitted with a Dorman Ricardo diesel engine and a five-speed box.

These were first successfully employed in the North African campaign, where they could traverse ground in which a wheeled machine would become bogged down. Fifty or so DB4 crawlers were used at Normandy immediately after the Allied beachhead was established there in June 1944 and their success in this exercise led to the Government ordering three large batches in 1944 and five batches in 1945. Undoubtedly, the DB4 tracklayer was seen as being useful for civilian purposes too. The rigours of war had shown the DB4 could take any amount of abuse, and it compared well against many of the American dozers, scrapers and crawlers that were flowing into Britain or which were sold as war surplus by the Americans after 1945. These ex-WD DB4s subsequently found employment in airfield work, forestry, road-making, and all-manner of reconstruction work projects in France, Holland and Belgium.

Beginning in 1948 a series of tracklayers, which included the TAK3 (tracklayer agricultural kerosene) and TAD3 (tracklayer agricultural diesel) and ITD3 (industrial tracklayer diesel), began to make their appearance. Immediately, they began making inroads into areas that had been formerly dominated by American manufacturers, but perhaps their greatest accolade was to beat the Yanks in the USA, for they were widely employed in the construction of the new Alaskan Highway. The success of the company's crawlers, both industrial and agricultural, gave rise to even greater efforts on behalf of the Marketing Department — the 'master' concept. So, in 1950, the crawlers became known as the 'Trackmaster', a designation that first appeared to the public at the Harrogate Convention that April.

Two years later, the TAD6 and ITD6 tracklayer came out with a six-cylinder diesel engine that produced a mean 50hp; it was offered with a choice of two track widths for either agricultural or industrial use. The following year it became known as the 50TD as part of a new designation scheme. This was a tractor that would stay in production until 1963 with a total of 1,667 models built. It was the company's first attempt at a six-cylinder diesel engine and, as such, it was to set a number of challenges for the firm's engineers, but it also gained many commendations and good reviews from outside sources.

A very early production Trackmaster model.

In 1953, with the introduction of the 30C and 30D wheeled tractors, the 30 series Tracklayers were introduced (these being the 30T, 30TD and 30ITD) and TAD6/ITD6 renamed as the 50TD/50ITD. Yet, despite their immediate success and total sales of 3,078 in the 30 series crawlers, it was a fickle market and highly specialised as the demand for major improvements went marching on. Even so, it was evident that even the bigger tracklayers were being sold into heavy industrial applications, which they were simply not suited for and the Service Department was facing a large number of requests for replacement clutches. The decision was, therefore, taken to examine the 50's clutch and gearbox to see where the problem lay and, as a result, the MkII 50TD appeared in March 1957 with a larger diameter clutch, new running gear and a substantially strengthened set of side-plates

A problem with 'clutch reliability' showed that the 30hp models were not up to the jobs that many contractors were expecting of them. Plans were made to up-rate them to a 40hp version and the first of these appeared early in 1960. However, due to the serious problems that were experienced after the 900 series wheeled tractors were introduced, a decision was taken not to produce immediately a 900 crawler version but to defer production and see where things went.

The desire for increased power was a major consideration for David Brown personally, and one day he announced that he felt that the company should have a 100hp crawler. In due course, the order was passed down to Herbert Ashfield to

An early model DB4, possibly from the first batch of 10. We are not quite sure how many DB4s were made altogether, but a figure of 110 is shown In some records as being the total number made before production ended on Wednesday 12 January 1949. Fitting these tractors with bulldozers, angle-dozers, scrapers and so on radically speeded up so many operations in this period of reconstruction. The crawler tractor was seen as being a revolutionary new force in both agriculture and civil engineering.

Below: Showing a few minor changes, especially in the seat, the prototype Trackmaster is still recognisable from the mock-up pictured below left.

Above: A tractor that just 'wooden go'. This timber mock-up in C Block at Meltham Mills in December 1947 shows the proposed design for the Trackmaster (complete with a chrome badge).

Below: The 50TD used in the film *Rockets Galore* being loaded at Oban for transportation to the Isle of Barra. The large lettering behind the seat was only put on this model for publicity purposes.

Below: The Trackmaster dozer prototype seen in Middlesex.

implement. He writes: 'In the 1950s we were producing light agricultural crawler tractors at Browns, but sadly these had a fairly narrow market. The trouble seemed to be that the dealers (and the Sales Department for that matter), kept overselling them into the industrial market where the equipment required 40hp against the 30hp machines which we had available. Now attached to our sales office we had a new market research department. It looked into the matter and recommended that, if we were to have any future in the crawler market, we should produce machines up to 100hp crawler capable of a top speed of 15mph. We simply did not have the resources to tackle the top end of the market, but I set about producing a prototype and decided to go for a really big machine to show everybody just what they had let themselves in for. After choosing a Leyland engine, we decided on a fabricated frame as being easier to construct than castings.

'When we came to the tracks, the quickest solution seemed to be to have a double sprocket and have

This 50hp model was used by the firm's Engineering Department and fitted with a very large protective cab. It was driven by Bill Sykes during the construction of E Block.

The unique 100hp Tracklayer, to which David Brown gave his tacit approval. However, when the Production Department went into the cost of the extra machinery and fitting shops required to build this crawler, the inevitable decision was reached not to go ahead. Nicknamed Goliath this one-off had no future and it spent its days being used as a dynamometer unit before it was eventually scrapped.

four links instead of two, enabling us to use DB existing parts. The steering would be clutch and brake. Having eventually completed the first machine, top management came and inspected it in the experimental fitting shop as the weather was bad. In the confines of the small shop, alongside 25hp agricultural tractors, it looked huge and its proportions frightened them to death: little wonder it became known to all concerned as Goliath! If mass production was to follow, it was declared that new machine and fitting shops would be required with bigger machine tools and heavier lifting equipment. At this stage David Brown had now to be brought back into the picture.

However, with a background of battle tank transmissions up to 700hp and marine transmissions for the navy running to several thousands of horse power, a mere 100hp crawler tractor looked very ordinary to him. He decided to fly up from London, and view the beast on the Crosland Moor airfield.'

Various experimental tracklayers followed the 30, 40 and 50 series, including the DB5 of which 11 were built. The 990T offered the promise of a modern tracklayer for continuing production well into the 1960s but this was not to be as Herbert Ashfield continues: 'As we entered the 1960s the tracklayers were becoming a really big problem for us, because at this point in time we were producing far too many models and variations for the quantity we were selling; in fact we were producing less and less, and more and more if you know what I mean. Our original agricultural Tracklayer had been designed for New Zealand, because that is where the demand was. In fact it was a very wide tractor, which had a 64in track I think, but it was very wide and you couldn't turn it over.

'It was well appreciated in New Zealand, because it was very steep and hilly and the thing would slide sideways before it would turn over. It also sold well into farming areas where they had heavy clay, which was obviously a good market. The big problem with our crawler was the fact that it was only a 30hp tracklayer, and all the equipment dozers etc that we had, were designed for the DB4 which was over 40hp. Things were getting worse and worse, and people were saying that our crawlers were no good, but it was simply down to the fact that the dealers and users were asking too much of them. On one occasion I had to go to the United States to sort out this type of problem, because they were putting very large dozers on to relatively small tracklayers. When they tried to lift them, the dozer blades just stayed on the ground and the tracklayer's nose came up.

DB5 Prototype (left) with a production DB501TD.

The 990T Tracklayer prototype on Meltham Moor.

'We also had a lot of trouble with some of the smaller dealers who, ready to make a sale at any cost, would tilt anything to them. We should have really designed our own dozers from the start although, in fact, we did ultimately do that. The 50TD six-cylinder crawler was less of a problem, and it sold very well in South America so we asked our dealers out there why this particular tracklayer sold so well; in reply they said "well, its big and red and noisy!" It was obvious by the 1960s that the demand for wheeled tractors was insatiable and we were making a profit on these, but we were making a loss on the tracked versions. Indeed these were a very difficult thing to produce, because our customers wanted industrial versions, wide versions, narrow versions etc; in fact you name it they wanted it. Ultimately, when Jack Thomson became Managing Director, we had a major inquest on the whole lot of our models. We were clearly over-extending our resources in so many ways and something had to give if we were to make an efficient organisation, so in 1963 we went out of tracklayers and concentrated entirely on wheeled tractors.'

AIRCRAFT TOWING TRACTORS: 1953-1958

The company's involvement with aircraft towing tractors, which began with the Air Ministry Tracklayer, was hardly the most auspicious of starts. However, by the time the company ceased production of its successor in the 1950s, the firm's reputation had been considerably enhanced not least of all through its industrial tractors. As Herbert Ashfield remembers: 'We kept on with the Air Ministry tractors until long after the war and it was always a pleasure to me when I was making a flight that the airport towing tractor would invariably be a DB even abroad. The last ones were made in 1958 but these lasted well into the 1960s and many even longer.'

The story of the Cropmaster variant, which appeared as the Taskmaster, is told later, but the success of these highly-dependable low-geared tractors was sufficient in its own right to justify the full confidence that the Ministry of Defence placed in the company. Yet, added to this came the bonus that here was an all-British tractor, which was another major plus point in those Cold War days of the early 1950s. It was an area that bred its own success, and the company did a lot of Ministry work for all branches of the armed forces, from towing heavy prototype planes at Farnborough to producing towing tractors for use on aircraft carriers.

Navy and RAF variants on test up the steeply graded Knowle Lane, Meltham. Note the work's Bedford K-type bus in front.

HRH Prince Charles 'drives' a Royal Navy towing tractor aboard HMS *Eagle* in 1956.

A Trackmaster 50 is seen here hauling a Klaas combine at the farm of Walter Winkley in South Yorkshire. The date of the picture is August 1952, and features the works' demonstrator LWU 345. This tractor was eventually loaned to British Railways as a ballast ripper, and was badly damaged following a collision with a freight engine during tunnel work near Hatfield in 1956.

Hell, Hull and Halifax so the saying goes, but this line up of 25 and 30 series tractors at Hull in 1956 could almost be heavenly. Bound for Scandinavia on board an Ellerman & Wilson freighter they were part of a substantial order that went to Finland and Sweden during the mid-1950s. The tractors, wearing Hunting Pink paintwork, were shipped to Hull Docks direct by rail from Meltham.

The first of the new generation of heavy towing tractors appeared in late 1952, when three prototype versions were produced for the MoD: naturally they were allocated to the three main branches of the armed forces, with one each going to the RAF, the RN's Fleet Air Arm and the Royal Corps of Engineers for evaluation. The tractors were a development of the Taskmaster, but they incorporated a number of features that had been demanded by the users, including an improved winch. They also featured the engine unit improved for the 30 series tractors.

This development saw the creation of a new aircraft-towing tractor available in two engine types: the diesel version being the 30ID and the petrol being the 30IC. A large number of these were purchased for the RAF and the FAA and these also incorporated special MoD requirements. Turbo models were also produced, as were heavy duty twin rear wheel versions and medium wheeled towing tractors. In total 320 aircraft towing tractors were built up to October 1958 when the 950 variant came out. After 1958 aircraft towing tractors were no longer available as a standard range, but industrial tractors continued the role for many years.

Showing the resplendent poppy red and yellow livery to very good effect is an experimental 850 being tested with an Albion baler at Meltham. The late Roy Morris, who probably tested the DBT range more than anyone else, reckoned that the 850 and 990 were the best tractors in the world and he said he would put them up against anything that was ever made before or since.

DBT's tractors were not all red, and to date several variants have been found. First of all there was 'battleship grey', a pale blue used on RN tractors such as this preserved model seen here. Then there came RAF blue, MoD olive, MoD sand, highway yellow, arctic flame (a bright orange), the Oliver green, Aer Lingus green, and midnight blue (used on the rocket ranges at Woomera Australia). Finally there were two painted purple and supplied to a customer in Africa.

One of the most dependable tractors to come out of Meltham Mills was the 880 Implematic. This example is owned by the Addy family from Marsh Farm, Shepley, Huddersfield, and 619 DWT carries Ben Addy's name on the side. The tractor is seen at the 1997 David Brown Tractor Club rally at Crosland Moor. The club continues to offer help and support to all owners of David Brown or Meltham-built Case tractors.

TASKMASTER MODELS: 1948-1965

As we have seen, there was such a demand for the industrial tractors, which the company had converted from the Air Ministry tractors, that the firm decided to adapt the VAK1C (or Cropmaster as it had become known) into its own purpose-designed industrial tractor.

It was a much simpler job than the Air Ministry conversions, and the company ran this industrial version of the Cropmaster under the name Taskmaster until 1953. Its primary application was as an industrial towing tractor, and as such it featured heavy-duty steering, wide mudguards and towing hitch; many were also provided with heavy-duty winches.

The company used several around its own works at Penistone, Lockwood and, of course, Meltham Mills. One of these tractors was regularly paired with a purpose-built servicing unit, which incorporated a fuel tank and delivery system, battery charger/electric starter and an air-compressor. It was used to start up tractors that were awaiting despatch and had stood in store alongside the football and cricket fields at the bottom of Meltham Mills Road; it was also used for recovering or restarting tractors that had failed whilst being taken up Meltham Mills Road and the Knowle on their primary road tests.

Other well-known industrial users of the Taskmaster included Rolls Royce, Swan-Hunter, Commer Motors and a large number of local authorities, including Halifax Borough Council who had placed an order for 12 cab-versioned models. Appearing as the VIGAR for the petrol-engine version and VIDAR as the diesel, some 500 Taskmasters were made in the period up to 1953.

It is jumping ahead of the rest of the story somewhat to discuss the engine changes that came about later, but as these innovations came about, the Taskmaster was progressively fitted with 30, 900 and 950 engine units and corresponding tin-work on the bonnet/engine covers. Even so, the same low styling, with heavy-duty mudguards and

The works' tug Taskmaster tractor seen here, as it often was, parked just outside the author's childhood home in Meltham Mills Road.

This is the Taskmaster prototype seen below the works on the football ground in 1948. Note its 'highway' appointments.

Sold to ICI in 1956 this shunting version Turbo Taskmaster is based on the 30 series tractor and fitted with a cab.

A Super Taskmaster 301D/2 with twin rear wheels pictured in 1957.

Here we see a Taskmaster based on the 950 model al Meltham goods yard in 1960.

bench seat were retained, and the family traits of the Taskmaster were continued through a succession of new tractors. In all some 2,752 Taskmasters were produced, with many and varied adaptations being made to suit industrial requirements all around the world. One of the most unusual variants was a forklift truck built for the Australian market. This model had a back-to-front driving position with the engine unit behind the driver, whilst the forklift was to the front of the driver and situated between the small rear wheels.

In many ways, the Taskmaster took off from where the crawlers had left off in 1963. For some this concentration on wheeled tractors was just a natural part of the process of progression and concentration on the firm's strong points. But industrial applications never went far from the minds of others. Tom Lazenby commented that there was a serious possibility of David Brown developing a joint range with JCB. Herbert Ashfield went to visit that firm, but was not given the best of receptions. Yet one wonders how the proposed 990T and 1010T might have performed had they been developed and put into service with a complementary range of associated equipment.

At one stage, after the new assembly line opened at Meltham Mills, the author was asked to do a costing exercise for the updating of the old assembly line for the production of special industrial wheeled and crawler tractors. The capital costs were not high, but they came at a time when the company was facing a very uncertain future after a crippling strike by its draughtsmen. The industrial assembly line plans died as a consequence and, within a very short time, the company was sold to the American multinational J. I. Case.

25 AND 30 SERIES: 1953-1958

By the early 1950s it became clear that the Cropmaster range of tractors, whilst still selling well, was beginning to face fierce competition from other manufacturers who were undercutting David Brown's list price. It was also clear that a new breed of tractor owner was emerging and, whereas the immediate post-war demand had been for bigger and heavier tractors of 30hp or more, there was now a growing trend to lighter tractors of 20-25hp.

A DB25, fitted with a common toolbar mounting a Spring Tine Cultivator, stands outside the factory's boiler house.

This was brought about because smaller farms, especially those that had not mechanised in the 1940s, were now finding it was time to do so. To continue to farm with only horse-power was very uneconomical by that time, and the smaller farms quickly began to convert — even those in very marginal upland areas. Thankfully new grant regimes assisted the poorer farmers to increase food production in Britain. This was greatly needed due to the food shortages, specially the meat ration, which had been dramatically cut by 1950. What is more, increased food production in Commonwealth countries, like Australia, saw export sales increase.

Now, whilst the Cropmaster was simply the best post-war tractor of its size on the market, Ford, Massey and other manufacturers began to realise that there was a growing market for smaller tractors, and it was a niche that the new Ferguson models very quickly began to exploit. If the Cropmaster was going to compete, it was evident that it would require new features in order to prolong its life. So the decision was taken to produce a stripped down version of the Cropmaster range, where certain cost savings in manufacturing could be passed on to the customer. One of the most obvious solutions was to produce a tractor with a smaller engine, and with a 25hp version immediate reductions could be made in the selling price. Meanwhile, economies in the manufacture of a 30hp version could also be achieved through careful design.

The DB25 prototype in 1952 heavily disguised and deliberately fitted with Cropmaster tinwork. This was a process that would later be perpetuated in the models that followed and all sorts of tractors ran round in guises that proclaimed them to be something entirely different.

The next stage in the DB25 story was a batch of five pre-production models built to evaluate the tractors under working conditions in order to get the bugs out before mass manufacture began.

As Leonard Craven recalls: 'In the early 1950s, as the post-war reconstruction period came to an end, the demand for tractors continued apace but the availability of supplies was much more widespread. In turn this depressed the agricultural market slightly, and after a decade of being able to sell anything and everything they made, tractor manufacturers found that prices were now becoming an important issue with many farmers. David Brown was no exception and the firm decided to produce the stripped down version of the Cropmaster.'

Fitted with fan-type fenders and single seats, the models became known as the 25 and 30 series tractors. In recalling their introduction. Herbert Ashfield writes: 'Ferguson came in with real mass production with Massey Ferguson, and later on Ford got going as well so we began to feel the draught a bit. My contention was that we should stop somewhere in between the 25hp Ferguson and the 40hp Ford. Unfortunately the problem with the Cropmaster and the Super Cropmaster was that they were getting as pricey as the Ford and farmers were getting less power for their money. So we did a strip down version, the 25 and 30. These were wonderful tractors, just right for British farmers. We easily undercut Ford, with a very modern tractor and at the same time produced a superior tractor to the Ferguson. They were designated by Mr David Brown as 25 and 30, which signified their nominal horse-power. He had decided that his name should figure large in the tractor's image, and that the "master" name detracted from the image of quality he felt the firm's name warranted. So out went the "Cropmaster" name, and David Brown came to the fore — but we were soon put at a disadvantage as a number of makers weren't as scrupulous in their designation numbers as we were, and added another five or even 10hp on to their designation number, giving customers entirely the wrong impression.'

This is the DB30 prototype fitted with a Tri-disc plough.

An experimental high-clearance 30D with mid-mounted tool bar. It was designed for the Californian market in 1954 but never put into full production.

The 25 and 30 series were some of Meltham's greatest secrets, and although some publications have claimed that the tractors went on sale in February 1953, we can put the record straight and state categorically that they were not released to the public until Friday 27 March when they went on show at the 1953 Harrogate Convention. At this event David Brown dealers and distributors were presented with the DB25, 30C and 30D. Other dealers were invited to the factory to view the new models as they came off the production line.

The 25 (later to be known as the 25C) represented the company's entry into the popular priced class, and was presented in such a way as immediately to appeal to both the small and the large-scale farmer. Powered by the 3.5in bore petrol or petrol/paraffin engine, it was fitted with a six-speed gearbox and the latest two-position hydraulic lift, the 25 brought Cropmaster performance and reliability within reach of those who could not hitherto afford it. For a comparatively low initial outlay, the small farmer could now purchase a powerful but economical tractor, which would be

The DB30 half-track, which sold well in Ireland.

capable of every job. The consideration that the farmer could continue to use his own trailed implements in conjunction with the decent drawbar on the 25 was well appreciated. This allowed him to mechanise his operations, and not be tied down to the immediate expenditure of purchasing mounted implements. It was a big difference, and it made the 25 a firm favourite with both the farming press and the small-scale farmers who bought it.

Another feature was the Traction Control Unit (TCU) that was a controlled weight transfer system and enabled even small tractors such as the 25 to carry out heavy work with large implements. As mentioned earlier, the 25 also appealed to larger farms, because of its low-price to high-performance factors making it a suitable choice for a general duty machine. Some farms purchased the single pan-seat 25 as a second machine, others sold their larger tractors and standardised on a small fleet of 25hp tractors. The appearance of the 30hp tractor in its stripped down version was also well appreciated, although at this time it did not look greatly different from the Cropmaster.

Indeed, one picture shows that the original 30 was fitted with Cropmaster tin-work and badged as such. However, the new 30, in both its engine configurations, was a remarkably economic tractor achieving a very high acreage per hour to low fuel consumption ratio. The change to a styling similar to the 25, incidentally came about a year after the introduction of the 30, and with this the famous DB bench seat finally disappeared from the standard market. However, well into the 1970s some of the company's tractors for the European market, especially Germany and Belgium, were still calling for bench seats and square-topped wide mud-guards on which people could sit as well.

VAD6 50D: 1953-1959

Early in 1953 another new product came out in the shape of the Cropmaster 50. It had been the long-held dream of David Brown to make a six-cylinder diesel capable of producing 50hp and with this it was hoped to provide a tractor which could break into, both the top end of the agricultural market and also the industrial one as well. It was an ambitious concept, and it owed its origins to the 50hp crawler of 1952 rather than the 30hp Cropmaster. Initially called the VAD6, the name Cropmaster 50 was employed more as a marketing concept, rather than specifically conveying the actual pedigree of the tractor. After it began rolling off the production line in January 1953, its initial market was aimed specifically at the company's export trade. The first major public appearance of this large towing tractor in Britain was at the Harrogate Convention in 1953, but by this time it had already undergone a sea-change and been renamed as the 50D.

Herbert Ashfield explains why the tractor was designed, as it seemed to be so much at odds with the company's stated policy of the day: 'The idea for the 50D came about because a lot of people in the organisation were saying we wanted a big wheeled tractor that was like a powerful crawler and fitted with a big six-cylinder engine. So we made a big engine and a transmission that was rugged enough to stand up to it, and on this power unit we developed the TAD6 crawler and then the VAD6 wheeled tractor.

The first DB50 is seen in the grounds of David Brown's house, at Durker Roods, Meltham. It was envisaged that this model would satisfy a demand for countries where tractors were needed to pull large trailers, specifically in South America and the developing countries of the Commonwealth.

'The DB50 was designed basically from scratch, and it wasn't related to any of the others; in fact, it was more closely related to the early DB4 tracklayers than it was to the Cropmaster. However, neither of these machines ever sold in quantity because a) we couldn't produce enough and b) the export market was a bit dodgy! In fact, we were selling more overseas than we were in this country, and it's always a bad policy to have a machine whose primary market is an export one. The trouble with an export market is you can't easily cure problems that develop with the equipment; but if you have a good home market, you can sort out the teething troubles on your own doorstep. The 50D sold quite well in South Africa, Australia and South America, in fact anywhere where there was a requirement for hauling big four-wheel trailers.'

The main problems lay with the head on the original six-cylinder engine, and because it was a single-piece unit it used to warp quite badly and blow the gasket between the cylinders if the engine was overloaded. It was a common fault, and it wasn't really

The 50D was unlike any other David Brown wheeled tractor, as it had no hydraulics but did have a side-mounted belt pulley and a four-speed PTO. Its six-cylinder engine had a $3^5/_8$in bore and a 4in stroke, and used many components that were employed in the Cropmaster. However, it was certainly not an uprated Cropmaster engine as some commentators have previously stated.

An experimental 50D tricycle tractor seen at Durker Roods, Meltham in 1953.

overcome until the 1970s when Herbert Ashfield devised an arrangement that employed two three-cylinder, cylinder heads on the six-cylinder block. Big, powerful and rugged it may have been, but it was not a popular model and in total only 1,260 were produced before construction was brought to an end in summer 1958. The market for a six-cylinder in this country had not yet developed sufficiently for the company to maintain confidence in the concept and develop it for a wider UK application.

Again. Herbert Ashfield provides another insight into the six-cylinder engine's demise: 'I felt we should go on with a six-cylinder and bring out a big tractor for the 1960s, but we would have had to make substantial improvements on our existing design. Unfortunately it was the cost of both tooling and the redesigning of the tractor that killed that one, so out went the six-cylinder idea. These development costs were so high that the management wouldn't pay for them, but even so they wanted a more powerful tractor. Over the years I kept planning ways that we could achieve this by turbo-charging, but we could never get a turbo-charger that could give the life we required so we continued on with a four-cylinder engine and waited for someone to come up with what we needed.' Accordingly the 50D went out of production and the six-cylinder DB tractor came to an end for the meantime, yet the 5OD itself has become a much sought after collector's piece thanks to its rarity!

900 SERIES: 1955-1957

Sadly, this model has often been quoted as David Brown's worst tractor, and it is true that it did earn itself quite a bad reputation. Yet, from the outset, it had been intended that the 900 should only be a stop-gap measure, before the firm began producing a tractor that would be suited to fast-advancing mechanisation in the agricultural world. Simultaneous with the introduction of the David Brown 900 came the time when the company began a new way in designating its various models.

As mentioned earlier, the DB25 and DB30 delivered that level of horse-power, and a bit more, but some manufacturers were not as scrupulous and their model numbers were marginally higher than the actual horse-power that the tractors delivered. David Brown was not prepared to indulge in this practice, even though it obviously influenced customers to buy certain types of tractor. The outcry, which came about when tractors failed to deliver the purported horse-power, subsequently led to the establishment of National Tractor Testing. The Marketing Department at Meltham Mills came up with the idea that the company should use a designation which in no way could be construed as horse-power, and because of this it devised the 900 numbering series.

In 1954 the company began experimenting with a new prototype, in which it intended to embody all the features needed to update the Cropmaster and its stripped down 25 and 30 successors. This was to be a completely new tractor, known as the VAD5. Herbert Ashfield drew once more on his recollections when asked how this came about: 'From around 1954/55, there was pressure for an entirely new design of tractor as the Cropmaster was supposed to be a bit dated. It must have been when it was a bit fiat at the works, as I was commissioned to design a basically new tractor. One of the things we had trouble with was the cast-iron frame, which was originally cast in just one piece: and,

A production 900 is seen with a pulverisor version of the company's forage harvester alongside Meltham Gas Works in 1955.

as there were only two foundries in the country that could cast it, we had real trouble in getting supplies at times. I talked this problem through with our Chief Designer, and we decided that the frame could be chopped in half and made in two pieces, which would (in turn) make it easier for small foundries to cast it. But this was only a temporary measure, and the idea that someone put forward was to copy the Fordson Major.

'This would have led to our having a steel sub-frame on which we could easily mount the engine and gain more flexibility in manufacture. However, as things turned out, it never worked out that way, but we did make various prototypes to test the idea. Another thing we wanted to do was get rid of the type of steering rod that we had used since the early days, so we made up a model with the steering over the top. It looked very American when it was finished, and it too never went into production. However, a lot of the ideas behind the VAD5 were ultimately incorporated in production of the 900. For example, we found that we could get the same features as we had in the existing line, by using the same castings and engine mounts, etc.

'When we came to the actual prototype of the 900, we also had a large number of new features that we wanted to incorporate, including: an adjustable heavy-duty front axle, which would give better steering geometry on the wider track widths; live PTO shaft and power lift pump were fitted to enable the equipment to keep operating when the tractor was stopped; weight transfer from implement to tractor rear wheels, namely traction control, which would prevent wheel spin under heavy loads; differential lock; hydraulic depth control for use with mounted implements lacking depth wheels; comfort seat (instead of the pan seat); revised styling and a dual colour scheme; batteries

This was the VAD prototype of 1954, with its American style over-bonnet steering. It never went into production but was the first step in the development of the 900 tractor.

This was the next stage. Here we see the VAD5G, which has no American look and resembles what will become the 900. In fact, it is believed that this and the previous picture were taken on the same day for comparative purposes.

positioned each side of the seat or in front of the radiator; a repositioned air cleaner behind the radiator grill instead of allowing it to hang on the side of the engine; and, a distributor injection pump on diesel engines, which was intended to be cheaper, smaller and give smoother running. Not all these features were incorporated and, due to the model's short life, some of these were actually carried over into the 950 or 990.'

During its launch at Smithfield, David Brown junior, said: 'Our policy must always be to give value for money — that is something about which we, as Yorkshiremen, are very particular — and we are convinced that the 900 tractor upholds that tradition.' With its twin range gear box giving six forward and two reverse gears, a two-speed PTO and pulley, improved one-piece bonnet styling, overload release, independent foot brakes and TCU it seemed to give good value for money. This was particularly pleasing when it was revealed that its ex-works price was just £593 10s, £42 10s less than the 30D. Providing extra output with greater economy, it should have been **the** tractor for the mid-1950s. However, it was not to be, for the 40hp 900 got off to a very bad start as a result of its new distributor injection pump, made by CAV, which was fitted to all diesel models. Although prototypes had been well tested, pumps on production models were prone to seizure.

Tom Lazenby recorded how the matter gave his sales department a major headache until it was finally resolved: 'The fuel pump on the 900 frightened us to death because of all the troubles it gave but we couldn't revert back to the in-line pump, because this couldn't work on the 900 and, although we still had the 25s and 30s in production, all we were building at the time were 900s. Things very nearly came to a full stop. The way things were going it could have ended in a spectacular lawsuit with CAV, and probably would have done if it hadn't been for an incident that transpired on Huddersfield station. Obviously we were trying hard to find what was wrong and so were CAV. Pumps were going up and down between Meltham and the CAV factory, going by rail, by wagon, by everything: just as they were coming back to us from overseas by air and by sea for reservicing. We just couldn't get the things to work, so we sent them back to the makers to see if they could. Oddly enough, CAV could get them to work again, but don't ask me how; because when they came back to us they began to fail again.

'By this time the night shift was lucky if it had half the pumps it needed to get it through to the morning, and the engines could not be left without pumps as the complete engine assemblies had to be tried on the test-bed. The strange thing was the pumps that were being fitted

Autumn 1954 saw the prototype 900 built.

would work on the engine test-bed and they didn't fail when the finished tractor was tested. It was afterwards when they failed — usually when they began their working lives, but an incident at Huddersfield station finally made it all become clear.

'Because of the acute shortage of pumps, CAV were managing to make sufficient one day to meet our production needs the next, but they had to send these up by passenger train. We used to send a van down to meet the trains from Birmingham that were carrying a box full of pumps. I don't know how big these boxes were, but one night, either the man in the train threw them out or they were dropped on the station platform with quite a bang! Our driver suddenly guessed that this could be what was causing the problem, so he brought them directly round to the Engine Test Department, and we put them straight on to test. None of them worked at all! So what was happening to make the pumps fail if they were dropped or banged?

'Well our engineers began to take a closer look at these pumps, and what they found was this. When they built the units CAV had used a component inside the pump and somehow, during the machining of it, it had built up stress. However, when you dropped them or put the pumps into regular service, it relieved the stress, the component jammed and the pump failed. Within days of making this revelation, we were out of trouble with that, but our reputation had taken an awful battering.'

Another problem noted in the 900 was found with the steering, especially after the safety authorities introduced a limit on the amount of play at the steering wheel rim and applied it enthusiastically to tractors. Herbert Ashfield noted: 'The limit was about 2in, I believe, but the 900 seemed to develop 2½in and stay there, so several new steering relay lever bearings had to be fitted to maintain compliance with this requirement. The plan to install a comfort seat was dropped, and while this kept the price down, it was not a feature that could be used by the salesman as a talking point. Then, in late 1957, a live power take off and power lift pump were introduced and this kept sales going, aided by the superior performance of the machine over the old Cropmaster range.'

In 1958 the company decided to not make any further improvements to the 900 and instead it designed the other outstanding features into the new model it was proposing, thereby making a clean break with the past. Thus, while the 25s and 30s were still being produced, the 900 went out of production in summer 1958, being superseded by the 950 that was free of teething troubles and enjoyed a good reputation from the word go. With the Livedrive versions that became an option during production run, some 13,770 900s were produced, including a small batch of tractors designated as 903 (a row-crop version for the Californian market). However, when the last of the blue-wheeled tractors was taken on a test run down Meltham Mills Road for the final time, there were more than a few people who were relieved to see the back of them.

VAD12, 2D SERIES: 1956-1964

One of the most unusual tractors ever built at Meltham Mills was the VAD12/V or 2D (as it was better known), which entered production in 1956 and lasted until 1961. This was a very small, lightweight tractor that featured a two-cylinder 14hp air-cooled diesel engine, which had been specially designed by the company, and had a mid-mounted tool carrier that carried a range of implements.

To tell the story of how the 2D was developed I enlisted the assistance of Derek Marshall and Herbert Ashfield who writes about its development: 'The Sales Director, Fred Marsh, cherished the idea of a low cost, 14- to 16hp tractor that he believed would sell to the small farmer still using animals. As a basis for our design I looked at the Massey Harris "Pony" tractor of orthodox design, which met the specification but it did not perform well under test, and so this particular project was stillborn. The Sales Director, however, did not give up easily and he bought an Allis Chalmers model "G" for us to inspect.

'This was a 12hp tool-frame tractor with the engine at the rear, tools in the middle and a hand lift. The driver sat in front of the engine and behind the tools. "It must have a power lift, it must be able to plough, and turn on its own length," said Mr Marsh as he rapidly outlined requirements which, while making it superior to the "G", would also make it more expensive. His eloquence, however, carried management with him and I was directed to produce a specification and design for such a tractor. When we tested the "G", we found it suitable for light cultivation only, its biggest problem was its petrol engine that stalled very easily. Another limitation was the excessive effort required to operate the hand lift, so we decided on a power lift. Being currently plagued by oil leaks on our standard hydraulic system. I opted for a pneumatic lift.

'Doubts were also expressed on a mid-mounted plough. "You can't push a plough!" seemed to be a fairly general opinion but we did not intend to push it, rather we pulled it from the front axle. We then produced a functional prototype to try out our suppositions. The engine became our next problem. Because of being rear-mounted, it overhung the back axle and any out of balance force resulted in excessive vibration. Small multi-cylinder engines such as the Ford car engine were acceptable as regards vibration but unacceptable because they stalled easily under varied loading. The small diesels that were available in the required power range were too much out of balance and indeed

The prototype 2D tractor fitted with a 10hp Ford E494A car engine winch, which, apart from stalling easily, performed satisfactorily under test.

almost threw the driver out of his seat. I, therefore, decided we must build our own perfectly balanced two-cylinder diesel with a heavy flywheel to avoid stalling. But, we adopted an unorthodox approach, because the reciprocating out of balance force created by a piston can only be perfectly balanced by a similar reciprocating force 180° out of phase. To achieve this we put the pistons in line and balanced them by a dummy piston in between and opposite, thus 180° out of phase. The engine ran smoothly, beyond our expectations and we had no further trouble with vibration, but to simplify the installation, we designed the engine to be air-cooled.

'It met our requirements in the field. It would not stall and could be run at low speed in high gear for light work — above all, from a sales' point of view, it was very practical because the fuel consumption was extremely low. Sales of production tractors started slowly, as the machine was viewed with caution by the farming community. On the other hand, the academic institutions, both home and abroad, were loud in their praise for the revolutionary layout.'

However, despite this great accolade, the tractor went through some difficult teething problems before it could be marketed, as Derek Marshall reveals: 'When the field tests began in earnest, we started with what was still a very basic unit as the engine and transmission units were not ready at this early stage. Consequently, as the first mock-up used for trial was devoid of the two main power units, the prototype was pulled along by another tractor. At first sight this might appear to be rather pointless but, to the contrary, this provided valuable information and data, which enabled us to make changes and improvements to the linkage geometry and steering even at this early stage. In view of the unique design and specification, it was intended to keep the project as secret and as far away from prying eyes as possible, although it was inevitable that locals and casual observers could see what was going on. However, we were obviously quite pleased at the secrecy of the exercise, even though we were sure that questions were asked about the sanity of two or three grown-up people dragging this weird object up and down the fields for no apparent purpose or results. When the Ford engine was fitted, the machine ran under its own power, and more meaningful tests could begin. During these tests two major problems arose and it became clear that these would need addressing before production could begin. Firstly, controlling the hand-lift mechanism with the implement attached (despite the adjustable balance springs) required a Herculean effort on the part of the operator. Whilst lowering the implement was not too bad, once it touched the ground, it was then necessary to overcome the full resistance of the springs in order to provide the required working depth.

In total some 2,008 2Ds were produced, with a large variety of special models appearing in short and long wheelbases, wide or narrow widths, and low or high clearance. There was even this one that had the look of a small conventional tractor when pictured at Lee Mills, Scholes.

Here we see a long wheelbased experimental unit that was eventually bought by John Scaife of Lincolnshire in 1963. He kept it in daily service in his nurseries for some 18 years.

'As this was almost an impossibility, we considered it was essential to provide some power assistance to the lift, and this was achieved very successfully by fitting a small compressed air pump. This we mounted directly to the front of the gearbox and pressure was fed to the tubular main frame that, when suitably adapted, provided an excellent air tank for the system. Secondly, depth control of the implement was still somewhat erratic, particularly with the long tool-bar or cultivator; a condition that appeared to be due to the fact that the two lift ropes controlling the depth (and being attached centrally to the tool-bar) allowed it to "yaw" or see-saw. Fitting a small depth wheel at the outer ends of the tool-bar overcame this problem, and also provided a more accurate control of the working depth.

'It soon became evident that the engine was well able to provide ample power, even under the most severe conditions but, once again,

The short wheelbased 2D was widely praised by the various agricultural colleges, and the farming press called it 'the tractor of the future'. A lot were sold in Holland and France as well as around the market gardens near London.

two fundamental problems had to be solved. The inertia start system as a unit worked reasonably well, but difficulties arose, however, under cold start conditions when the engine invariably failed to pick up before the inertia unit wound down; in turn this required the operator to continue frantically cranking to effect a start. As the starting problems continued, a major (and much welcomed) change was made at this point with the development and introduction of a full electric system, including starter, alternator and full lighting. We considered this to be a necessary requirement, and we were delighted with the satisfactory and meaningful tests, which resulted in only a few alterations or changes being required.'

The old hank-winding shed at Meltham Mills had meanwhile been converted to a special assembly line for the 2D, and production began shortly after the tests were completed. The tractor made its first public appearance at the Smithfield Show in December 1955 where it was promoted as 'A multi-purpose machine to work on any farm or horticultural holding.' However, as the 1960s dawned, it became clear that the sales targets were not being achieved. Herbert Ashfield was asked why this was, and he recalls: 'The 2D never sold in the quantities originally forecast, but we were receiving orders for all sorts of modified machines that only sold in small quantities to specialist markets and incidentally with a profit margin that took no account of the extra overheads incurred in producing them. Admittedly, it was very popular in places but it was when it was sold to a big farm that the troubles began, because the farmer wanted all sorts of elaborate equipment, hoes, etc. Sadly the 2D never really took off as David Brown and Fred Marsh imagined it would, even though all the institutions and universities said this was the tractor of the future.

'In 1961 the Managing Director, Jack Thomson, instituted an enquiry in to the question of why they weren't selling. So I looked at it very coolly and the first thing I did was to ask how many salesmen they had trying to sell standard tractors and how many were selling 2Ds. I found out it was taking about three times the salesman hours to sell a 2D as opposed to that taken to clinch a deal on a standard tractor. So, talking to both my field test personnel and farmers, I found that many users were wanting a rear-mounted linkage and they were buying small second-hand tractors. This meant that the enemy of the 2D was the second-hand Fordson, Ferguson and David Brown, so if the farmer could buy a good used tractor for about the same as they were paying for a new 2D, he would probably go for a machine with rear-mounted linkage.'

950 Series: 1958-1961

As seen, the 900 only ran three years and, rather than completely replacing the DB25s and 30s, it was produced alongside them until they also finished in 1958. Meanwhile the 950 started production in that year, so the company had three main models running concurrently, a rather chaotic situation for both the production and sales teams. Production of the 950 began on Monday 28 October 1958, but it was decided to wait for the turn of the year to announce the launch and, for marketing reasons, not to do it at the Smithfield Show.

Accordingly, with the awkwardness of the 900 behind it, and having seen what other manufacturers had already done with their 'tractors for the 1960s' it was David Brown's turn for a two-venue launch. These launch celebrations were carried out on opposite sides of the world, with David Brown senior performing his launch at the Canadian Farm & Industrial Trade Fair in Toronto, and his son presiding over a DB function in Harrogate. This launch took place on 28 January 1959 and it presented what was apparently a completely new design. In reality it was the MkII 900 but it embodied all the features that David Brown had intended to put into that model had it not had such a disastrous start in life!

The 950's principal features, and all of them standard, were: an exceptionally easy steering unit with a very small turning circle; high ground clearance; full road and field lighting (with a rear-mounted floodlight); screw-type lift rod and geared levelling lever; adjustable front and rear wheel widths (from 52in to 76in in 4in steps); fully adjustable drawbar: universal linkage for category one or two implements; new type gear pump; large 11.00 x 32 rear tyres; power take-off and belt pulley; simplified TCU to prevent wheel-spin: independent foot brakes; adjustable overload release; steering column throttle control; and the 'Super-Comfortable Driving Seat'. Its $3^{1}/_{2}$in bore engine produced 42.5bhp, but extensive field tests had already proved its economy in operation. In addition there was also a 950 Livedrive model, with 'live' power take-off and a 'live' hydraulic system. Optional extras were: power steering; three-way isolator valve providing instant selection of the main or two auxiliary services; and, a linkage drawbar for light towing duties.

It was a marvellous tractor, presented on a marvellous stand that had been based on the award-winning display that the company had used at Smithfield the preceding month. At the opening of the Toronto show, David Brown was accompanied by his wife and four full-blooded Indian Chiefs and two Indian Princesses. After the ceremonies, these natives made David a full Chief of the Iroquois tribe, an honour that had been bestowed upon few English visitors — indeed, the previous personality to receive this accolade was Her Royal Highness Princess Margaret.

The popular little 950 was a real boon for the company; here the late Tom Lazenby, on the far left, is seen showing the tractor to customers during brake tests in Knowle Lane.

This quite remarkable photograph at Scar Bottom Mills shows the 950 prototype; this tractor was originally code-named the VAD11. The view was taken in 1958 despite the fact that the tinwork shows a styling a decade ahead of this era. Indeed this styling is significantly similar to the tinwork fitted to David Brown models when the livery changed in 1965.

Although the 950 was produced with the styling shown, a decision had been taken to introduce a new style of tractor for the 1960s. This was planned for the 990/880 models. However, it was decided to defer this until the introduction of the Selectamatic range.

At the British launch, Mr J. B. Townley, Managing Director of distributors Barton Motors (Preston) Ltd, said: 'We have seen today what I call a thundering good tractor, which represents a tremendous endeavour on the part of the David Brown company to present us with a fine product at a very competitive price. With this tractor we have really got something.' The farming press was just as enthusiastic about it, and one of the Canadian papers said: 'The 950 is a triumph for David Brown. This little company from England have taken on the American giants and beaten them. The result is a new tractor that has come about because the company has been listening closely to its customers on farms all over the world. The result is a machine to suit all markets.'

Tom Lazenby recorded the introduction of the 950 with a great deal of pride, saying: 'The problems of the fuel pump and steering on the 900 gave us no end of trouble, and we lost a lot of customer confidence because of that. In the end it made us bring forward the 950, which was really the 900 with a bigger set of wheels, which went up from 28s to 32s. It was a sort of Mark II 900, but it had a little bit more filling here and there. But, because it was the same tractor really, we had to make a lot of changes in how it looked and performed. Messrs Ashfield & Co in the Engineering Department had solved the problems of how the tractor worked, but we had the job of selling it, and we had all on to overcome the problems of customer confidence which the 900 had given us. We had to make a tractor that had instant sales appeal, and then get away from the blue colour, which David Brown junior had chosen for the 900's wheels and radiator grille. So one Saturday morning five of us assembled at the works, including the Managing Director (Jack Thomson), George Shannon, Alan Walker and somebody from production. When we got there they had got a series of tractors lined

This is an early cabbed version of the 950 at Meltham station goods yard. The railway line to Meltham opened in 1868, and closed to passenger trains some 80 years later. However, the railway was extensively used by the company for both the receipt of components and raw materials and also the despatch of complete tractors. Once the railway closed in 1965, much of the goods yard was taken over by the company and part of the old line became a test track.

up with different coloured wheels, including the yellow ones. After some consultation and debate we decided that the yellow ones best complimented the red livery, and Jack Thomson said "Aye that'll do, we'll never pick that ***** awful blue again!"'

Herbert Ashfield recalls what happened next: 'Because of the problems with the 900 we went straight on to the 950 and this tractor incorporated all the improvements that we'd planned to put in the 900. The 950 was a cracker right from the word go, and it sold ever so well, in the end we made 5,574 of the 950 T and U series, but it was the Implematic version which really did well. In all we sold 18,125 of the V and W, and A and B versions of the 950.' In December 1959 the company brought out a revolutionary development of the standard tractor, in the shape of the Implematic. This was, in many ways, a remarkable innovation, as it set about addressing a problem that many farmers had been facing since the principle of mounting equipment on tractor linkages was first developed in the 1930s. For a long time manufacturers were divided on how the working depth of an implement should be controlled.

Some people favoured a depth wheel whilst others employed a form of automatic draft control. Generally tractors were designed to operate one type of equipment or the other, but not both. This resulted in the poor farmer having his choice of equipment restricted, and it was a situation that remained deadlocked until David Brown introduced the Implematic. At the 1959 Smithfield Show, the 950 Implematic (V and W versions) went on display, featuring an ingenious modification to the hydraulic system that permitted the operation of dual implement types, plus differential lock — and all at no extra cost! Simplicity was the keynote of the new system, with a single lever controlling both the choice of implement type and the TCU. To cater for implements without a depth wheel, the company introduced Traction Depth Control, an arrangement in which the top link was spring-loaded and, when in work, was under compression from the draft forces acting on the implement. This compression of the top link actuated, via a Bowden cable, the movement of a hydraulic valve. For any given control lever setting, the implement goes into work until the set draft is achieved.

When the ground conditions varied, the draft automatically increased or decreased, as did the pressure on the top link. In turn this caused the hydraulic valve to move; for example, when the draft increased, it allowed more oil to be pumped into the lift cylinder that raised the implement and then restored the draft to the preset level but, when the draft decreased, oil was released from the cylinder thus allowing the implement to go deeper. This automatic regulation of the implement was occurring all the time it was in work, and thus saved considerable resetting time and a lot of man hours. When the tractor was using implements with a depth wheel, the hydraulic system operated in exactly the same manner as before. With this feature the 950 became even more popular, and it soon erased the painful memories that the 900 had bestowed and all concerned were hard pressed to cope with the demand.

Indeed 1960 turned out to be a record year for the Meltham Mills works, and David Brown junior promised: 'We are going to build more tractors at the Meltham factory than we have ever built before.' Yet this may have seemed an overly optimistic hope, especially in view of the fact that there was an overall 16% decrease in the sale of tractors in Britain that year. However, whilst other manufacturers were tightening their belts, David Brown went on to achieve a record output, and by February the despatch of tractors was up a remarkable 50% on the same period the previous year. Salesmen could not keep up with the demand, and all over the world farmers were having to wait for their new machines. Extra labour was recruited for the Meltham and Leigh works, and by May the production had been dramatically increased. By September output had reached an all-time record, and 80% of production was going for export.

In the midst of this success, the 850 was launched and David Brown also entered into an agreement with the Oliver Corporation of America to make two types of tractors on its behalf, one of which (the model 600) was based on the 950. The final improvements to 950 appeared as the A and B versions in October 1960 (in time for Smithfield) and these included additional refinements to what was already a 'world-beating tractor'.

850 SERIES: 1961-1965

Whilst the 950 was taking care of the main end of the market, the company remained conscious of the fact that a smaller tractor would have a ready appeal. As we have seen Jack Thompson had already decided to discontinue the 2D in the latter part of 1960 and secretly a decision had been taken to introduce a small three-cylinder diesel tractor of conventional appearance in its stead. As Herbert Ashfield writes: 'As we came on with the 950, we began to look at the fact that there was a need for a smaller tractor. We decided to designate this the 850, and aimed for between 30 and 35hp. Obviously, we needed a new power unit for this machine, and one of the things we looked at was the Perkins three-cylinder engine.

Seen at Wistaston, near Crewe, in 1960, a 850 and 950 pose with the four-ton Garrett steam tractor of 1906 belonging to Hugh and Sam Jackson who were the local David Brown Tractor dealers in that part of Cheshire.

'It influenced our thinking quite a lot, but having decided that a three-cylinder engine was cheaper to make in smaller powers than a four-cylinder we began to design our own three-cylinder engine to put in the 850.' However, it was to be some time before this unit was ready, and as the 2D was to be phased out, it was decided to bring in the four-cylinder 3½in bore engine producing 35bhp into a smaller version of the 950. Like its big brother, it was available in petrol (VAG2A model) and diesel (VAG2B model) forms, although these later gave way to the C and D variants in September 1961 when the 850 Implematic was given a new multi-speed PTO.

At the same time a decision was taken to discontinue the petrol engine, but, because orders were still flowing through the system, the last petrol version did not go down the assembly line until June 1962. By spring 1963, the C and D models were seeing further developments, first with the introduction of a new, fabricated front axle and then with the facility of height control. In October 1965 serial number 317439 rolled down the assembly line, and production of the 850 finally came to an end. In many ways it was a stop-gap measure that could service the market at its smaller end until the three-cylinder 880 arrived, but in the meantime it was a delightful and highly effective tractor in its own right and 14,242 were produced.

Not only was the 850 of interest to the company's smaller customers around the world but it also appealed to big ones as well. In October 1959 representatives from the Oliver company, a famous American tractor manufacturer, came to Meltham to evaluate the 950 tractor in action, and they were highly impressed with what they saw. They were also to make several successive visits to view the new 850.

Herbert Ashfield tells how the deal came about; he writes: 'We were looking to sell more tractors in North America and oddly enough we were successful in both Canada and California,

This is a somewhat unusual machine based on the 950 but sporting tinwork for the Oliver 500 (otherwise the 850). According to the late Tom Lazenby, this one was made especially for evaluation by Oliver and sent to America three months before the main order. Herbert Ashfield recalls that the Oliver order was clinched when their Sales Director said 'You know we like your little tractor, well, would you do it in the Oliver livery and let us sell it for you?' Lazenby continued: 'Obviously we said yes, and designed some cosmetic changes to its appearance and put in a few modifications which they wanted and it did very well. We were still increasing our sales with Oliver when Ford sacked all its franchise dealers in the USA and started supplying tractors through its own distributors, but it was also very short of a small tractor. Accordingly the ex-Ford dealers came to Europe to find a tractor to sell and they chose David Brown, and we couldn't turn down this business as it meant that we had a complete US franchise, but it also ended our Oliver deal.'

but we couldn't get into the Mid-West of the USA where the real big market was. Now, we'd always kept in contact with the American manufacturers but originally they used to sort of laugh at us. We were viewed very much as the poor relations. Then Oliver's suddenly found themselves in trouble with their little machine, they couldn't make it economically enough because they just hadn't got a big enough market.'

On one of their visits the author's uncle (John Glew) was given the privilege of taking them to the field-tests in the firm's mini-bus. On one of their visits, representatives from Oliver were so impressed with what they had seen they 'could hardly contain their excitement on the way back to the works.' A deal was subsequently signed, and Oliver began to market the 850 and the 950 in America, where they were respectively designated as the 500 and 600. Finished in a distinctive green and white livery, the first Oliver rolled off the line on Friday 26 February 1960. Yet, despite the close tie-in with Oliver, this in no way affected existing David Brown dealers in either North or South America. The first consignment of 500s and 600s left Meltham station on a special train, hauled by Black Five 4-6-0 No 45101. The train of 49 Oliver tractors left on Thursday 10 March for Salford Docks, where they were loaded on to MV *Manchester Progress* for delivery to Chicago via the St Lawrence Seaway. In the next few months a further 217 tractors followed the route of these pioneers. It was good business and would eventually see the combined sales of 2,148 DB-built Oliver tractors.

880 SERIES: 1961-1965

The 880 Implematic was also introduced in September 1961 and, although this model would run concurrently with the 850 until October 1965, it had already been viewed as its natural successor when the three-cylinder engine became available. At first the 880 appeared with a four-cylinder engine, and some 12,685 of these were to be built. Yet its greatest success came as the smaller engined version, which was introduced in September 1964 and went on to see 39,900 examples of its type. Many people may wonder, however, why the company thought it practical to run the 850 and 880 at the same time.

An 880 seen with a loader adapted for pallet lifting; this particular picture was taken during a joint demonstration with ICI.

Robin Kedward worked with the tractor over a many years and became a devoted fan. In 1997 he wrote: 'Some farmers wanted a tractor of the same size as the 850, but with increased power, so the 880 was an ideal solution and correctly advertised as the ideal solution for the "one tractor" farm. It was very similar to the 850, but with eight stud wheels (some of the last 850s were also eight stud), the tall higher clearance front axle, which was far less prone to wear than the short type used on the 850 and 950 and, of course, the well proven 42.5hp engine from the 950 although production of that model only continued until December 1962.

'The 880s were offered with 11/49 (high speed) or 9/50 (low speed) final drives, although I've never seen an 880 with the latter. All the 880 models had bowl-less fuel filters, which made servicing easier, and the oil filter was mounted directly onto the cylinder block, dispensing with the aluminium filter head. Also, for the first time, I believe, the yellow stove enamelled exhaust was used. This tractor was an immediate success. With its easy starting and economical engine, swinging drawbar and two speed PTO, giving superb performance, these little tractors would often out-perform larger models and many spent their working lives driving balers, rotavaters and rotaspreaders. March 1963 brought the introduction of the fabricated front axle, which was fitted first to serial number 355065 and later went on to be used on many other models. The following month saw tractor number 355341 being the first 880 to benefit from the introduction of height control. This tractor remained basically the same until the final four-cylinder 880 rolled off the production line in August 1964, the last one being graced with the serial No 362382.

'August 1964 also brought dramatic changes in the engine department with the introduction of a new three-cylinder power unit of a completely new DB design. The AD3/40 series had a cross-flow cylinder head, a bore of $3^{7}/_{16}$in a $4^{1}/_{2}$in stroke and an unusually mounted vertical injection pump. These models were now called the E and F series and commenced with the serial No 521001 in September. My own 880 three-cylinder is No 521196, which makes it one of the very first. Along with the new three-cylinder engine, which had a much higher torque than the old four-cylinder, came other changes; for example, the battery was changed to a single 12V instead of the two 6Vs and was now located at the front of the radiator, whilst the air-cleaner was moved from its time honoured position on the left-hand side of the engine to a similar position in front of the radiator. A new type of three-way hydraulic valve was also fitted and after a few months the engine was also fitted with a high-

This photograph hears the caption 'The first production 850 Implematic', but it may actually be a prototype as the view was taken in December 1960.

lift camshaft, which again improved performance. Plans were already underway for a new model with a much improved hydraulic system (Selectamatic) and this tractor was to be a proving ground for the new three-cylinder engine.'

With all these new features, plus continual improvements, there is little wonder that the 880 sold so well; yet when we look at the price list for December 1964 we can see another very good reason why farmers would choose it. The price list issued for the Smithfield Show informs us that the 880 Implematic Livedrive with 5.5 - 16 fronts and 12.4/11-28 rears cost just £72l.7s.6d whilst the 12-speed version was a little more expensive at £752.l2s.6d. The three-way valve U578 cost £7.5s.0d and linkage stabilisers at £1.10s.0d each. Those were the days!!

Sadly Poppy Red and Primrose Yellow gave way to Chocolate Brown and Orchid White, and in October 1965 the last 880 Implematic to be built was No 527521. In four years 19,207 880 Implematic tractors were produced, four-cylinder, three-cylinder and narrow models, but as many of the narrow models were primarily aimed at the export market, this version of the tractor (like the 850 Narrow) is very rare indeed. Yet, around the world, owners are still putting these tractors in regular use. Robin Kedward said: 'We have had a three-cylinder model for the last 26 years and not once has it ever let me down! Six months ago I managed to buy a nice four-cylinder model. It's impossible to say which of these models is the better. I like the quietness and smooth running of the four-cylinder, but I also like the slogging ability of the three-cylinder. As for fuel consumption and ease of starting there's nothing between them but I still have a soft spot for my old faithful three-cylinder!'

990 SERIES: 1961-1968

In October 1961, the Implematic range was improved and upgraded by the introduction of the 990 that, in the years that followed, would prove itself to be one of the best tractors ever to come from Meltham. It was very similar to the 950, but it benefited from a bigger clutch, stronger back-end, heavier castings and a new type of engine with a cross-flow cylinder head.

Again Robin Kedward noted: 'What an engine this turned out to be! It retained the 3in bore of the 950/880 but, with a much longer stroke of 4in, it developed 52.5hp at 2,200rpm. It was a power unit that would just laugh at rotaspreaders, wizzlers and forage harvesters. With that extra half inch of stroke this was. in my opinion, an engine with real "guts" — the harder you drove it the better it went. The 990 was sometimes criticised for its slow road speed (same as the 950), but I always thought this was more than made up for with the rest of the gears. No matter what you did with it, the 990 always had the perfect gear for the job.'

A 990 Implematic pictured on timber work in Scandinavia.

The matter of gearboxes is continued by Herbert Ashfield, who writes: 'The gearboxes on this new range of tractors were just about as perfect as we could get them, and they were as reliable in service as anything we had made thus far and they really reflected the long tradition of David Brown's gear-making. But the other thing I have to mention is the automatic gearbox that we eventually brought out.

'Before it was introduced we'd done a torque amplifier, which was like a Laycock De-Normanville overdrive on a car, but we did it the other way around. Instead of giving an overdrive, it gave an underdrive. So in effect you got a two-speed shift automatic, which split your gears: this gave a 12-speed gearbox and you also had a gear that went in-between each gear on the gearbox. This meant that, if you were ploughing and the tractor began to pant a bit, you could drop a gear without de-clutching or if you encountered a sticky patch this would pull you through. Now from that we developed even further, because I realised that if you put two torque amplifiers together, you could get a four-speed automatic gearbox. We worked on this box, I should think, about three or four years before we overcame all the problems because we were in uncharted territory. We required free-wheels and hand-brakes and all sorts of odd things on which we had no production experience. Because of this we wanted to be really certain that we'd got all the bugs out, so it was to be quite a while before we put it into full production. However, we did have a number of 990 prototypes and they were so reliable, and very few problems were encountered. I know to this day that there are a lot of the production models working around here yet.'

This was the first 990 prototype, and it is recorded in the grounds of Meltham Hall in July 1960. It will be noted that, other than the Implematic badge, the tractor is devoid of any markings. It also carries a number of 950 parts. On this point the late Roy Morris stated: 'Quite a number of 990 Implematics were produced in 1960, and they were sent to a variety of places for test. I took two down to our farm in Buckinghamshire, where they were put on to ploughing duties in the early autumn. By early 1961 we were on with testing the 990 Selectamatic and, despite what some people may say, this tractor was intended for introduction very early in the 1960s, with a completely new design of bonnet. However, there were a few snags with the Selectamatic process, and as the 990 Implematics were selling well, the top brass decided to hang fire a while.'

The 990 went on to appear in a number of variants. One of the most interesting developments and one that featured strongly in the company's marketing policy was the introduction of a highway tractor. The move into the semi-industrial market — against people like JCB and Massey Ferguson — was another area. This is a Highway version filled with a loader, digger and extendible hydraulic stabilisers outside the stable block at Meltham Hall in 1960.

The high-clearance and low-clearance versions of the 990 seen at Helme in 1964.

The first model to leave the factory was No 440001 and, as with its counterparts, it could have been fitted with either five- or six-stud front wheels as the six-stud front wheels were not yet standard. Two 6V batteries were fitted under the seat, the same as previous models, but the air-cleaner was now located in front of the radiator. All 990s had six-stud rear wheels and were fitted with 11-32 tyres, although 13-28 were an option. This tractor sold like hot cakes from the word go and production was soon stepped up to meet demand; as a result the 950 series was phased out in December 1962. April 1963 soon arrived and along with it came No 453124, now fitted with height control. In August 1963 No 455561 saw the introduction of the fabricated front axle, which was a great improvement on the previous tractors which were all fitted with the tall forged variety.

In August, more dramatic changes were to take place as a single 12V battery was now fitted in front of the radiator and the wheel-base lengthened by two inches. So, those who are thinking of restoring a later model 990, beware, the bonnet from an early 950 or 990 will not fit due to it being two inches shorter. A novel feature around this time was the fact that the now redundant battery boxes were fitted with different lids and became toolboxes. Two months later, in October, 12-speed transmission was offered as an option. More minor changes took place in early 1964 and, commencing with tractor No 461120, the glass fuel bowl beneath the fuel tank was dispensed with in favour of a different type of lift-pump and a straightforward push-pull tap. Beginning with No 463764 the company began fitting a key-start on the right-hand fuel tank support instead of the key and buttons on the left. However, more radical changes were on the way and, in May 1965, the 990 versions with the toolboxes beneath the seat disappeared and a new seat and seat support were introduced.

Also fitted were different mudguards, which were now bolted directly onto the rear axle and final drives. There was also a different drawbar, pick-up-hitch, three-way valve and the biggest change of all was the rear axle casing. The Selectamatic hydraulic system was obviously on its way and this latest type of axle casing was made in such a way as to facilitate drilling the required holes for this system. However, the holes were initially blanked, but it was obvious that the castings were being made in readiness for the change and the later Implematic castings even had a blanking plate for the dump valve! Were any of these ever fitted retrospectively with the Selectamatic hydraulic system one wonders?

The Selectamatic was to be a great success, and one which would continue through the years ahead; however, by early 1965, things were beginning to change, not least in the desire to introduce a new body shape and colour scheme. The advances with the 990 beyond 1965 are covered in the companion volume on David Brown Tractors from 1965 to 1988, but in October 1965 the last 990 Implematic (No 480600) rolled down the line. In just over four years 40,600 990s had been produced, including some non-Livedrive and industrial models with twin-plate clutches. It was a remarkable record that, at one stage, accounted for 50% of production.

The 1964 price list shows the 990 Implematic Livedrive with multi-speed PTO. and live dual purpose extra lift hydraulics at the modest sum of £784.9s.0d, and the 12-speed model at £815.14s.0d. Some of the accessories were priced as follows: Foot throttle U377 £2.12s.6d; three-way hydraulic-valve U279 £l0.0s.0d; pick-up-hitch U385 £l2.15s.0d; and, a quite expensive £54.15s.0d for power steering. Many farmers came to David Brown for the first time with the 990 and with the company they stayed until Case ended production at Meltham Mills. It was a tractor that bred real customer loyalty, but this loyalty was not easily won and it was satisfaction with the 990 that really put this model head and shoulders above its competitors.

The export of half-track versions of the 990 to Scandinavia was common; this particular example is seen in Finland.

A Conclusion and New Beginning –
The 770: 1965-1970

To conclude this book and set the scene for the next, we will consider the 770, which was introduced in 1965 and thus beyond the time scale of this volume, but as it appeared as a red tractor we trust you will forgive this slight transgression beyond our 1964 cut-off date. As Herbert Ashfield recalls: 'The problems with the 2D started David Brown's thinking could we produce a small standard tractor at a reasonable price? So we sat down and got all the figures out and looked at the profit margin on the 2D. These showed us that if you took the standard overheads you were making a profit on the 2D, but when you added all the extras such as extra salesman hours and what not you were actually making a loss. So out went the 2D and in came the 880s and later we developed the 770, which we did in narrow and low-clearance versions and this took over a lot of the 2D's functions. The 770 was a really superb lightweight tractor of conventional design and relatively low enough in price for the small farmer and it could therefore compete with the second-hand 30hp tractors from Ford and Ferguson.'

Before the 770 a small tractor, the 750 or U447, had been built exclusively for the German market between 1962 and 1964. Total production of this model was 279 so it hardly forms part of our story, but its concept was important in the later development of the 770. The first production 770A was launched in January 1965, and 1,831 red tractors were built before they went on to the white model that was up-rated to 36hp.

Opposite: This 770 was the very first to be built, appearing in May 1964. This picture was taken near Denby Dale under great secrecy. The tractor arrived by road with rather decrepit looking tinwork, but soon a fitter's van turned up, and the 770 was quickly converted to its proper guise. After the photographer had done his job, back on went the disguise, leaving the farm owner quite bewildered by the speed of it all.

Index